A FIRST COURSE IN STATISTICS

Dexter J. Booth MSc PhD FIMA
Senior Lecturer, Huddersfield Polytechnic

DP PUBLICATIONS LTD.
12 ROMSEY ROAD
EASTLEIGH
HAMPSHIRE SO5 4AL
1987

Acknowledgements

The author wishes to express his gratitude to;

The London Chamber of Commerce and Industry
The Royal Society of Arts

for their kind permission to reproduce a number of questions set on their past examination papers. Gratitude is also expressed to **The Daily Telegraph** for their permission to reproduce certain pictures that have appeared amongst their pages.

ISBN 0905435-84-2

Printed in Great Britain by
The Guernsey Press Company Ltd.,
Braye Road, Vale,
Guernsey, Channel Islands.

PREFACE

AIM

1. The aim of this book is to provide a course text for introductory level courses in Statistics. It provides comprehensive coverage of the first examinations in Statistics of the Royal Society of Arts and the London Chamber of Commerce and Industry. In doing so, it is also suitable for many other introductory Statistics courses including those of certain GCSE Boards and BTEC. Apart from its main intended use as a course text, the book is designed as a self-study manual for anybody wanting an introduction to the subject.

NEED

2. The need was seen for a book which assumed of the reader no prior knowledge of statistics whatsoever and no more than an ability to handle simple arithmetic.

APPROACH

3. In order for the reader to understand the subject as a **whole,** before seeing where each **element** fits in, the first section provides an overview of the subject by tracing the execution of a typical statistical project from conception to completion. The project chosen being one with which **everyone** can readily identify.

Within this section the basic elements of Statistics are identified in an introductory form. Subsequent sections deal in detail with these basic elements.
The book always builds on **known** information. At no time is a statistical concept introduced before the ground has been thoroughly prepared and the **need** for it demonstrated. At the end of each Chapter there are summaries, review questions, graded exercises and examination questions. Answers to **even numbered** questions are provided at the end of the book. **Odd numbered** questions are intended to be used in classwork and answers to these are provided to lecturers (free of charge) applying to the publishers on departmental headed notepaper.

CONTENTS

SECTION 3 COLLECTION OF DATA

SECTION 4   DERIVING THE STATISTICS

Correlation, Amount of correlation, Measuring correlation, The product moment correlation coefficient, Spearman's rank correlation coefficient, The limitations of correlation.

SECTION 5   COMMUNICATING THE RESULTS

Dedication

To Liz, Olivia, James and Bruno for their patience and understanding.

Section 1 This Is Statistics

By looking at a complete statistical enquiry this first Section lays the foundations for the remainder of the book. The first Chapter deals with the fundamentals of data, statistics and statistical enquiries in general. It is shown that any statistical enquiry can be separated into four distinct tasks. Each of these tasks then forms the subject of the subsequent four Chapters where each task is discussed in brief within the context of a single Statistical Enquiry.

There are five Chapters in this Section. They are;

Chapter 1	:	**Fundamental Ideas**
Chapter 2	:	**Asking The Question**
Chapter 3	:	**Collecting The Data**
Chapter 4	:	**Deriving The Statistics**
Chapter 5	:	**Communicating The Results**

1 Fundamental Ideas

INTRODUCTION

1 In this short introductory chapter the terms DATA and STATISTICS are defined. These are fundamental to what is defined as a four-part STATISTICAL EXERCISE.

There are four major parts to this Chapter. They are;

> **Input and Output**
> **A Statistical System**
> **Data and Statistics**
> **Statistical Enquiries**

INPUT AND OUTPUT

2 If steak is put into a meat grinder the end result is mincemeat The meat grinder PROCESSES the steak that is put in and ejects it as mincemeat. This system of processing steak into mincemeat can be illustrated by the following diagram

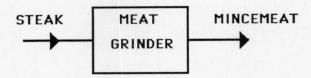

The arrows show that steak is put in and mincemeat comes out. The box represents the process that changes steak into mincemeat.

3 A diagram like this can be used to illustrate any system that has an INPUT and a PROCESS that acts on this INPUT to produce an OUTPUT.

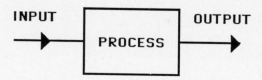

4 There are countless systems that can be illustrated in this way. For example, if we put the numbers 5 and 6 into an ADDING PROCESS the numbers 5 and 6 are added together to give 11. The number 11 is the output.

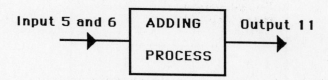

The system of interest in his book is the STATISTICAL SYSTEM.

A STATISTICAL SYSTEM

5 A Statistical System provides ANSWERS to QUESTIONS.

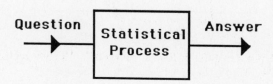

DATA AND STATISTICS

6 A question is fed into the statistical process in the form of numbers. These numbers are called DATA. The statistical process manipulates the DATA to produce the answer. The answer is also in form of numbers. These numbers are called STATISTICS.

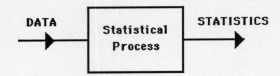

The answer to any given question may be in the form of one or many statistics - it all depends upon the question.

EXAMPLE 1

The following table gives the weights of six people;

NAME	WEIGHT (Kg)
Alice	54
Eddy	73
Charles	76
Fiona	51
Diana	53
Brian	68

The question posed is;

"Who is the heaviest and who is the lightest?"

The DATA are the recorded weights on the right hand side of the table. The data is PROCESSED by putting the weights in ascending order

NAME	WEIGHT (Kg)
Fiona	51
Diana	53
Alice	54
Brian	68
Eddy	73
Charles	76

This process produces the TWO statistics **51 Kg** for the lightest and **76 Kg** for the heaviest. Referring to the names it is concluded that **Fiona is the lightest and Charles is the heaviest.**
Had the question posed been;

"What is the total weight?"

The answer would have been in the form of a SINGLE statistic **375 Kg** - produced by the process of adding all the weights together.

STATISTICAL ENQUIRIES

7 The two previous worked examples are very simple but they each contain all the parts of a STATISTICAL ENQUIRY A STATISTICAL ENQUIRY has four parts. They are;

    1 Asking The Question
    2 Collecting The Data
    3 Deriving The Statistics
    4 Communicating The Results

The manner in which these four parts link together can be illustrated by the following diagram;

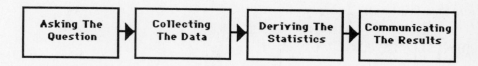

8 In the first example the question ASKED was "Who was the heaviest and who was the lightest?". The data was COLLECTED by weighing all six people. The statistics were CALCULATED by arranging the data in ascending order. This produced the weights **51 Kg** and **76 Kg**. By looking back at the data the names **Charles** and **Fiona** were then COMMUNICATED as the result.

EXAMPLE 2

How many more times has the word 'the' appeared than the words 'a' and 'an' up to and including Paragraph 8 of this chapter? Indicate each process of the statistical exercise as it is completed.

1 <u>Asking The Question</u> How many more times does the word 'the' appear than the words 'a' or 'an' together up to and including Paragraph 8

2 <u>Collecting The Data</u> - Count the number of appearances of the relevant words. The word 'the' appears 63 times and the words 'a' and 'an' appear a total of 13 times.

3 <u>Deriving The Statistics</u> - subtract 13 from 63 to give 50.

4 <u>Communicating The Results</u> - The word 'the' appears 50 times more than the words 'a' and 'an' together.

SUMMARY

9 A STATISTICAL PROCESS provides answers to questions. The questions are put into the statistical process in the form of numbers called DATA. The answers are provided by the statistical process in the form of numbers called STATISTICS.
A STATISTICAL SYSTEM is the complete system of QUESTION - PROCESS - ANSWER.

A STATISTICAL ENQUIRY has four parts to it;

> **1 Asking the question**
> **2 Collecting the data**
> **3 Deriving the Statistics**
> **4 Communicating the results**

The statistical system was introduced to allow the words DATA and STATISTICS to be defined. The four-part Statistical Enquiry is the more important idea and will be the one referred to in the remainder of the book.

KEY POINTS TO NOTE

10 Data, Statistics, Statistical enquiry

STUDENT SELF TESTING

SELF REVIEW QUESTIONS

1 Describe what is meant by a statistical system. (3-5)

2 Describe briefly the differences between Data and Statistics. (6)

3 Describe the different parts of a statistical snquiry. (7,8)

EXERCISES (Answers begin on Page 249)

In the following three problems indicate what the data is and what the statistics are. Indicate also, the four parts of the statistical enquiry.

1 The number of times that it rained on a particular day during a given year in Nutwood and Bruddersford are recorded in the following table;

DAY	NUTWOOD	BRUDDERSFORD
Monday	5	17
Tuesday	9	12
Wednesday	20	6
Thursday	15	5
Friday	10	4
Saturday	4	18
Sunday	6	16

Which of these two towns would you choose to go for;

a) a weekend holiday?
b) a midweek holiday?

2 On seven successive weeks a salesman drove from Manchester to Leeds. The times of his journeys were as follows;

WEEK	TIME (Min)
1	59
2	68
3	65
4	62
5	58
6	70
7	63

Which week took the longest and which took the shortest time? What is the total travelling time over the seven weeks?

3 A die was rolled 500 times. The numbers 1 to 6 came up according to the following table;

FACE NUMBER	FREQUENCY
1	50
2	50
3	60
4	50
5	90
6	200

If you were to bet on a particular number on the next roll of the die which number would you choose? Why?

2 Asking The Question

INTRODUCTION

1 In this chapter the first part of a statistical enquiry is considered in the context of a real problem - the Statistics teacher at a local Comprehensive School sets his students a project. In ASKING THE QUESTION the need to clarify the question is discussed.

Therte are two major parts to this Chapter. They are;

Asking the Question
Clarifying the Question

ASKING THE QUESTION

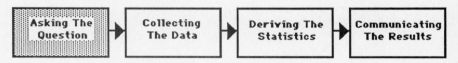

2 Every year the West Linton High School holds an Annual Open Day in July. This year the Statistics teacher had decided that his Fourth Formers were to perform a Statistical Enquiry and to display their conclusions at the Open Day. He was unsure of what sort of problem to consider until one day he heard two children boasting to each other about their pets. One little girl claimed to have more than the other whereupon the other countered that she had fewer brothers and sisters so the comparison was not fair. This overheard conversation provided the teacher with his inspiration. He decided that his Fourth Formers were going to find out if indeed there was any connection between the number of children and the number of pets in a household.

The following lesson he told the class of the project and they discussed how they were to set about it. The first aspect of this statistical enquiry that had to be settled was the actual question they were to answer. Eventually, the decision made was to ask;

"Is the number of pets in a household related in any way to the number of children in that household?"

CLARIFYING THE QUESTION

3 The teacher pointed out that at this stage certain matters had to be cleared up before they could accept the question as it stood.

Firstly, what is a pet?

One member of the class related how his dog had just given birth to a litter of six puppies so his house's pet population had increased dramatically. Since they did not want the answer to the question to depend on when the question was asked it was decided not to consider animals that were only temporary visitors. Another member of the class objected to the word 'animals' - he had a pet spider that he loved dearly and wanted that to count as well. Finally a 'pet' was decided to be a 'permanent pet' - one that would be expected to be kept in the household until it died naturally.

Secondly, what is a child?

Since the legal limit of childhood is 18 years, this problem was easily cleared up. A child was considered to be any person who was 17 years old or younger.

The third point concerned which households were to be considered. The entire population of the town was out of the question - it was far too large. After some discussion the class eventually settled on the households in the local housing estate. It was a reasonable size for the class to cover door-to-door. Furthermore, since a large number of the school's students lived there and were known, they should not meet much objection when gathering the data.

Finally, the question was re-phrased;

> **"Is the number of permanent pets in a household related in any way to the number of people 17 years old or younger in the same household on the Benevue Estate?"**

MORAL

4 Alhough the original question appeared to be straightforward there were uncertainties in it. The question to be asked must be clear and precise. If it is not clear and precise then it must be clarified until it is.

This completed the first part of the Statistical Enquiry.

5 The teacher ended the class by telling them that he would go to the public library and obtain a copy of the estate's street plans. These would give the location and addresses of each house. From this information he could then allot specific houses to each class member for them to approach. Before he dismissed the class he asked them to give some thought as to how they were to set about collecting the data which is the next part of the statistical enquiry.

SUMMARY

6 When phrasing a question that is the object of a statistical enquiry the meaning of the question must be clear and precise. If it is not clear and precise then it must be clarified until it is.

KEY POINTS TO NOTE

7 Asking the Question. Clarifying the question.

STUDENT SELF TESTING

SELF REVIEW QUESTIONS

1 Why must the question to be answered by a statistical enquiry be clarified? (3,4)

EXERCISE (Answers begin on Page 249)

Each of the following are questions that could be asked in a Statistical Enquiry. Describe briefly how each could be clarified and re-phrase them.

> 1 "How many children do families have?"
>
> 2 "How many books do households borrow from the public library?"
>
> 3 "How much television do people watch?"

3 Collecting The Data

INTRODUCTION

1 This third chapter deals with the problem of collecting data for the statistical enquiry introduced in Chapter 2. In COLLECTING THE DATA simple rules are given for constructing a QUESTIONNAIRE.

There are three major parts to this Chapter. They are;

>**Collecting the Data**
>**Constructing a Questionnaire**
>**Gathering the Data Together**

COLLECTING THE DATA

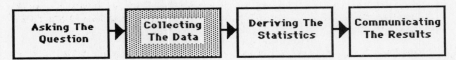

2 Two days later when the class next met the teacher had all the information that he had promised. The public library had allowed him to copy all the relevant maps and the class now had a complete layout of the streets and houses on the estate. There were 204 houses and with a class of 34 students that meant each student was to be responsible for collecting the data from 6 houses.

Because people are very wary when individuals knock at their front door it was agreed that the students approach individual households in pairs. The class were asked to arrange themselves in pairs ready for the next class when the allocation of houses to students would be made.

Meanwhile they were to consider the best way of approaching a household. The idea of simply knocking on the door and asking questions was rejected for two reasons. Firstly, there would be no guarantee to the householder that the enquiry was genuine. Secondly, householders who were out would be missed and of those who were in some may find it inconvenient to answer questions at that particular time. It was decided to use a **QUESTIONNAIRE**.

CONSTRUCTING A QUESTIONNAIRE

3 A **QUESTIONNAIRE** is simply a printed list of questions. The questionnaire is usually left with the person who is required to answer the questions. This allows the answers to be filled in at leisure. The questionnaire should explain exactly what the object of the enquiry is. It should be short and its questions precise. It should also contain instructions telling how and when the completed questionnaire will be collected. With these requirements in mind the class eventually constructed the following questionnaire.

West Linton High School
39 Highway Road
Linton   **5 June**

On the 8th July the West Linton High School will be holding its Annual Open Day. This year the students of the Fourth Form have decided to perform a Statistical Enquiry and to display their findings at the Open Day.

Your cooperation in the enquiry is vital and the class would greatly appreciate your answers to the questions listed below. Your name and address will not be recorded against your replies so complete confidentiality is assured.

The question the class wishes to answer is;

> "Is the number of permanent pets in a household related in any way to the number of people 17 years old or younger in the same household on the Benevue Estate?"

To enable the students to solve this problem please answer the following questions;

1. How many people 17 years old or younger live in your house?
   _____

2. How many permanent pets live in your house? _____
   (A permanent pet is any living creature that you call a pet that is
   expected to live with you until it dies naturally. This does not
   include temporary pets such as litters of offspring that will be
   disposed of)

In anticipation of your cooperation the class would like to thank you. You are cordially invited to the Annual Open Day to view their conclusions.

THIS QUESTIONNAIRE WILL BE COLLECTED BETWEEN 7 pm AND 8 pm NEXT MONDAY

4 The questionnaire was written on the School's headed notepaper to show that it was a genuine request and the complete confidentiality of those answering the questions was assured. A number of people object to being identified so this was an essential assurance. The households were given a weekend to answer the questions and the time of collection was set at a time when most people were likely to be at home.

By the time the class met on the following Friday the questionnaire had been duplicated. Specific houses had been allocated to specific students. The entire class then walked together to the Benevue Estate and delivered their questionnaires.

When the students collected the completed questionnaires they had been instructed to ask the householder's permission to check the answers. By going through the questions with the householder personally any errors in the answers stood a good chance of being detected. It also allowed the students to answer any queries raised by the householder. In this way more accuracy could be achieved.

GATHERING THE DATA TOGETHER

5 The next Wednesday saw the class returning their completed questionnaires. Of the 204 households questionned, 200 had responded and 4 had either refused or could not be contacted. The next task was to gather together the data contained on all the questionnaires.

On each questionnaire the relevant data consisted of a pair of numbers. The first being the number of children and the second the number of pets in a household. The teacher had decided that each pair of numbers could be written inside brackets;

(Number of Children , Number of Pets)

The filled in brackets would then be referred to as DATA ITEMS to distinguish them from the original data contained on the questionnaire. To this end he produced a large sheet of paper containing 34 sets of six empty brackets arranged in columns. Each student was to be responsible for transferring the data from his or her six questionnaires to a set of brackets.

When the class had re-assembled the students transferred the data from their questionnaires to the sheet. The completed sheet is given below.

WEST LINTON HIGH SCHOOL
STATISTICS PROJECT

TABLE 1 DATA FROM QUESTIONNAIRES   **JUNE**

(NUMBER OF CHILDREN , NUMBER OF PETS)

```
( 0 ,1 ),( 0 ,1 ),( 0 ,2 ),( 1 ,0 ),( 1 ,3 ),( 1 ,0 ),( 0 ,2 )
( 2 ,1 ),( 0 ,0 ),( 0 ,2 ),( 2 ,2 ),( 1 ,3 ),( 0 ,0 ),( 0 ,1 )
( 4 ,5 ),( 2 ,1 ),( 0 ,0 ),( 0 ,0 ),( 3 ,2 ),( 2 ,1 ),( 2 ,3 )
( 2 ,3 ),( 3 ,2 ),( 2 ,3 ),( 2 ,2 ),( 4 ,2 ),( 1 ,0 ),( 2 ,1 )
( - ,- ),( 3 ,2 ),( 2 ,2 ),( 3 ,3 ),( 1 ,1 ),( 0 ,2 ),( 1 ,2 )
( 2 ,2 ),( 2 ,2 ),( 2 ,2 ),( 1 ,0 ),( 2 ,1 ),( 2 ,3 ),( 3 ,3 )
-----------------------------------------------------------------
( 3 ,1 ),( 1 ,1 ),( 0 ,0 ),( 1 ,1 ),( 0 ,0 ),( 0 ,1 ),( 2 ,1 )
( 2 ,2 ),( 1 ,2 ),( 2 ,1 ),( 5 ,4 ),( - ,- ),( 3 ,3 ),( 0 ,1 )
( 1 ,1 ),( 3 ,3 ),( 1 ,2 ),( 2 ,1 ),( 2 ,1 ),( 3 ,3 ),( 2 ,3 )
( 0 ,0 ),( 2 ,2 ),( 2 ,2 ),( 2 ,2 ),( 2 ,3 ),( 1 ,0 ),( 1 ,1 )
```

14

```
( 2 ,2 ),( 1 ,1 ),( 1 ,3 ),( 3 ,3 ),( 3 ,3 ),( 2 ,2 ),( 2 ,2 )
( 0 ,0 ),( 2 ,4 ),( 1 ,2 ),( 2 ,1 ),( 0 ,0 ),( 2 ,1 ),( 2 ,2 )
--------------------------------------------------------------------
( 3 ,1 ),( 2 ,1 ),( 1 ,0 ),( 2 ,1 ),( 2 ,1 ),( 2 ,2 ),( 1 ,0 )
( 1 ,1 ),( 2 ,2 ),( 0 ,1 ),( 2 ,1 ),( 0 ,2 ),( 1 ,1 ),( 2 ,1 )
( 0 ,1 ),( 0 ,1 ),( 0 ,1 ),( 0 ,0 ),( 2 ,3 ),( 3 ,3 ),( 2 ,3 )
( 2 ,1 ),( 2 ,1 ),( 3 ,3 ),( 0 ,1 ),( 1 ,1 ),( 2 ,4 ),( 1 ,0 )
( 0 ,0 ),( 1 ,2 ),( 2 ,3 ),( 2 ,0 ),( 3 ,3 ),( 1 ,2 ),( 3 ,2 )
( 1 ,2 ),( 1 ,0 ),( 2 ,1 ),( 2 ,3 ),( 2 ,2 ),( 1 ,2 ),( 2 ,1 )
--------------------------------------------------------------------
( 6 ,4 ),( - ,- ),( 0 ,2 ),( 0 ,0 ),( 0 ,0 ),( 2 ,2 ),( 0 ,0 )
( 1 ,3 ),( 0 ,2 ),( 0 ,0 ),( 3 ,3 ),( 1 ,0 ),( 4 ,4 ),( 0 ,1 )
( 1 ,0 ),( 2 ,2 ),( 4 ,0 ),( 1 ,0 ),( 1 ,0 ),( 2 ,2 ),( 1 ,3 )
( 3 ,1 ),( 2 ,1 ),( 1 ,0 ),( 0 ,1 ),( 1 ,2 ),( 0 ,2 ),( 2 ,1 )
( 3 ,2 ),( 2 ,3 ),( 3 ,3 ),( - ,- ),( 2 ,1 ),( 2 ,2 ),( 0 ,0 )
( 1 ,1 ),( 1 ,3 ),( 1 ,1 ),( 3 ,1 ),( 3 ,2 ),( 0 ,1 ),( 1 ,0 )
--------------------------------------------------------------------
( 0 ,1 ),( 2 ,1 ),( 0 ,1 ),( 2 ,1 ),( 1 ,1 ),( 2 ,2 )
( 2 ,2 ),( 2 ,1 ),( 1 ,0 ),( 5 ,2 ),( 1 ,0 ),( 2 ,1 )
( 0 ,1 ),( 4 ,4 ),( 0 ,1 ),( 0 ,0 ),( 1 ,1 ),( 0 ,2 )
( 2 ,3 ),( 2 ,3 ),( 1 ,2 ),( 0 ,1 ),( 1 ,3 ),( 1 ,1 )
( 3 ,3 ),( 2 ,1 ),( 1 ,0 ),( 0 ,0 ),( 2 ,1 ),( 3 ,2 )
( 1 ,0 ),( 2 ,2 ),( 3 ,3 ),( 2 ,2 ),( 0 ,1 ),( 4 ,4 )
----------------------------------------------------------
```

The entries (- , -) represent questionnaires that were not completed.

This concluded the second part of the Statistical Enquiry.

Deriving the statistics is the third part of the statistical enquiry and this aspect is dealt with in the next chapter.

SUMMARY

6 When constructing a questionnaire the following simple rules must be kept in mind;

> **1 The object of the questionnaire must be clearly stated.**
>
> **2 The questionnaire should be short and its questions clear.**
>
> **3 The questionnaire should clearly state how it is to be collected**

When collecting a completed questionnaire it is adviseable to check through it with the person who answered the questions. This helps to eliminate any errors in the answers. Many questionnaires are, of course, sent through the post. In such cases it is not possible to check each questionnaire with the individual involved.

When gathering data together from a set of completed questionnaires it is best to list the information in a table. The table should be headed with a title to indicate exactly what it contains. The entries into the table should be arranged as neatly as possible to enable the table to be easily read.

KEY POINTS TO NOTE

7 Collecting the data, Questionnaire

STUDENT SELF TESTING

SELF REVIEW QUESTIONS

1 What is a questionnaire? (3)

2 Why is a questionnaire better than door-to-door interviewing in person? (2)

3 What are the three simple rules to be followed when constructing a questionnaire? (6)

4 How would you gather together all the data from a set of completed questionnaires? (5,6)

5 Give two essential properties of a table. (5,6)

EXERCISE (Answers begin on Page 249)

In each of the following questions decide how you would construct a questionnaire to collect the required data.

1 How many students possess electronic calculators?

2 How often do people visit the cinema?

3 How many newspapers do people read?

4 Deriving The Statistics

INTRODUCTION

1 This Chapter deals with the third part of the statistical enquiry and introduces the three new concepts of CATEGORY, FREQUENCY and AVERAGE. The data items gathered from the questionnaire in Chapter 3 are re-arranged to put them into a more mangeable form. This is done in three stages. Firstly the data items are arranged into CATEGORIES. Secondly the FREQUENCIES of the data items in each category are counted and listed in FREQUENCY TABLES. In the third stage a final FREQUENCY TABLE is constructed where the AVERAGE numbers of pets per household are derived. Finally, from this last frequency table the answer to the original question posed in Chapter 2 is given.

There are six major parts to this Chapter. They are;

> **Deriving the Statistics**
> **Re-arranging the Data**
> **Frequency Table**
> **Average**
> **The Answer**
> **Comments on the Answer**

DERIVING THE STATISTICS

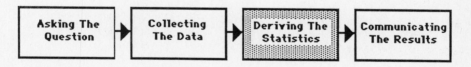

2 Deriving statistics from data is a process that involves many stages. The data has to be re-arranged to make it more mangeable and this re-arrangement may involve more than one stage. Once the data has been re-arranged the statistics can then be derived.

RE-ARRANGING THE DATA

3 The 204 data items in Table 1 of Chapter 3 were written in by the students as the data was read off each questionnaire. As a result, the data items are haphazardly arranged with no order at all. In their present state they are of little use for deriving statistics. What is required is some order amongst the data items and to achieve this they must be re-arranged.

The first stage in this re-arrangement is the separation of the data items into CATEGORIES. A CATEGORY is a group of items where each item possesses some feature in common with all the other items in the group. The Categories used in this statistical enquiry are the TYPES OF HOUSEHOLD and the common feature will be THE NUMBER OF CHILDREN in the household.

Category 1 will contain all those data items relating to households with no children. These data items all have a zero as their first number.

Category 2 will contain all those data items relating to households with one child. These data items all have a 1 as their first number.

This process continues up to **Category 7** which contains all those data items relating to households with 6 children. These data items all have a 6 as their first number.

In Table 2 below the data items have been re-arranged into Categories.

WEST LINTON HIGH SCHOOL
STATISTICS PROJECT

TABLE 2 RE-ARRANGED DATA ITEMS   **JUNE**

(NUMBER OF CHILDREN , NUMBER OF PETS)

CATEGORY 1
```
( 0 ,1 ),( 0 ,1 ),( 0 ,2 ),( 0 ,2 ),( 0 ,0 ),( 0 ,2 ),( 0 ,0 )
( 0 ,1 ),( 0 ,0 ),( 0 ,0 ),( 0 ,2 ),( 0 ,0 ),( 0 ,0 ),( 0 ,1 )
( 0 ,1 ),( 0 ,0 ),( 0 ,0 ),( 0 ,0 ),( 0 ,2 ),( 0 ,1 ),( 0 ,1 )
( 0 ,1 ),( 0 ,0 ),( 0 ,1 ),( 0 ,0 ),( 0 ,2 ),( 0 ,0 ),( 0 ,0 )
( 0 ,0 ),( 0 ,2 ),( 0 ,0 ),( 0 ,1 ),( 0 ,1 ),( 0 ,1 ),( 0 ,2 )
( 0 ,0 ),( 0 ,1 ),( 0 ,1 ),( 0 ,1 ),( 0 ,1 ),( 0 ,1 ),( 0 ,0 )
( 0 ,2 ),( 0 ,1 ),( 0 ,0 )
```

CATEGORY 2
```
( 1 ,0 ),( 1 ,3 ),( 1 ,0 ),( 1 ,3 ),( 1 ,0 ),( 1 ,1 ),( 1 ,1 )
( 1 ,2 ),( 1 ,0 ),( 1 ,1 ),( 1 ,1 ),( 1 ,2 ),( 1 ,1 ),( 1 ,2 )
( 1 ,0 ),( 1 ,1 ),( 1 ,1 ),( 1 ,3 ),( 1 ,2 ),( 1 ,0 ),( 1 ,0 )
( 1 ,1 ),( 1 ,1 ),( 1 ,1 ),( 1 ,0 ),( 1 ,2 ),( 1 ,2 ),( 1 ,2 )
( 1 ,0 ),( 1 ,2 ),( 1 ,3 ),( 1 ,0 ),( 1 ,0 ),( 1 ,0 ),( 1 ,0 )
( 1 ,3 ),( 1 ,0 ),( 1 ,2 ),( 1 ,1 ),( 1 ,3 ),( 1 ,1 ),( 1 ,0 )
( 1 ,1 ),( 1 ,0 ),( 1 ,0 ),( 1 ,1 ),( 1 ,2 ),( 1 ,3 ),( 1 ,0 )
( 1 ,0 )
```

CATEGORY 3

(2 ,1),(2 ,2),(2 ,1),(2 ,1),(2 ,3),(2 ,3),(2 ,3)
(2 ,2),(2 ,1),(2 ,2),(2 ,2),(2 ,2),(2 ,2),(2 ,1)
(2 ,3),(2 ,1),(2 ,2),(2 ,1),(2 ,1),(2 ,1),(2 ,1)
(2 ,2),(2 ,2),(2 ,2),(2 ,3),(2 ,2),(2 ,2),(2 ,2)
(2 ,4),(2 ,1),(2 ,2),(2 ,1),(2 ,1),(2 ,1),(2 ,2)
(2 ,2),(2 ,1),(2 ,1),(2 ,3),(2 ,3),(2 ,1),(2 ,1)
(2 ,4),(2 ,3),(2 ,0),(2 ,1),(2 ,3),(2 ,2),(2 ,1)
(2 ,2),(2 ,2),(2 ,2),(2 ,1),(2 ,3),(2 ,1),(2 ,2)
(2 ,1),(2 ,1),(2 ,2),(2 ,2),(2 ,1),(2 ,3),(2 ,3)
(2 ,1),(2 ,1),(2 ,2),(2 ,2),(2 ,1),(2 ,3),(2 ,1)

CATEGORY 4

(3 ,2),(3 ,2),(3 ,2),(3 ,3),(3 ,3),(3 ,1),(3 ,3)
(3 ,3),(3 ,3),(3 ,3),(3 ,3),(3 ,1),(3 ,3),(3 ,3)
(3 ,3),(3 ,2),(3 ,3),(3 ,1),(3 ,2),(3 ,3),(3 ,1)
(3 ,2),(3 ,3),(3 ,2),(3 ,3)

CATEGORY 5

(4 ,5),(4 ,2),(4 ,0),(4 ,2),(4 ,4),(4 ,4),(4, 4)

CATEGORY 6

(5 ,2),(5 ,4)

CATEGORY 7

(6 ,4)

4 The second stage in the re-arrangement of the data items concerns each individual Category. If you count the data items in Category 1 you will find there are 45. If you look closely you will see that there are only THREE DIFFERENT TYPES of data item, namely (0,0) , (0,1) and (0,2). Each of these data items are repeated to make up the total of 45. The data item (0,0) is repeated 18 times as is (0,1) and the data item (0,2) is repeated 9 times. The number of times a data item is repeated is called its FREQUENCY

The FREQUENCY of (0,0) is 18, the FREQUENCY of (0,1) is 18 and the FREQUENCY of (0,2) is 9

Using this idea of frequency, the contents of each Category can be neatly summarized by using a FREQUENCY TABLE.

FREQUENCY TABLE

5 A FREQUENCY TABLE is a table that records data items and their frequencies. Below is the completed frequency table for Category 1.

CATEGORY 1

DATA ITEM	FREQUENCY
(0,0)	18
(0,1)	18
(0,2)	9
TOTAL	45

Notice how this table is constructed. There are two columns, **each separated by a vertical line.** Each column is headed by **a clear description of what it contains.** These are two requirements for constructing clearly understood tables. A further requirement is that **entries into the table must be in well defined rows.**

At the bottom of this table is a row labelled **TOTAL** and the number **45.** This refers to the total number of households in Category 1 and it is obtained by adding up all the frequencies immediately above it. Make sure that you understand why this is so.

6 Using this table it is now possible to derive **the total number of pets in all the households in Category 1.** The number of pets in a household is given by the second number in the data item. For example, the data item (0,1) represents a household with no children and one pet. There are 18 such households so the total number of pets in familes with no children and one pets each is

$$1 \times 18 = 18 \text{ pets}$$

The data item (0,2) represents a household with no children and 2 pets. There are 9 such households so the total number of pets in households with no children and 2 pets each is

$$2 \times 9 = 18 \text{ pets}$$

These numbers are recorded in the following table which is the old Category 1 frequency table extended by one column.

CATEGORY 1

DATA ITEM	FREQUENCY	NUMBER OF PETS
(0,0)	18	0
(0,1)	18	18
(0,2)	9	18
TOTAL	45	36

Notice how the numbers in the third column are obtained by multiplying the second number in the data item by the frequency. Make sure you understand why this is so. The bottom row contains the number **36**. This is the total number of pets in all Category 1 households. It is obtained by adding up all the numbers immediately above it. Make sure that you understand why this is so.

The frequency tables for the remaining six Categories are listed below. Check the frequencies with the data items in Table 2 and make sure that you agree with all the numbers written down.

CATEGORY 2

DATA ITEM	FREQUENCY	NUMBER OF PETS
(1,0)	19	0
(1,1)	14	14
(1,2)	10	20
(1,3)	7	21
TOTAL	50	55

CATEGORY 3

DATA ITEM	FREQUENCY	NUMBER OF PETS
(2,0)	1	0
(2,1)	29	29
(2,2)	25	50
(2,3)	13	39
(2,4)	2	8
TOTAL	70	126

CATEGORY 4

DATA ITEM	FREQUENCY	NUMBER OF PETS
(3,1)	4	4
(3,2)	7	14
(3,3)	14	42
TOTAL	25	60

CATEGORY 5

DATA ITEM	FREQUENCY	NUMBER OF PETS
(4,0)	1	0
(4,2)	2	4
(4,4)	3	12
(4,5)	1	5
TOTAL	7	21

CATEGORY 6

DATA ITEM	FREQUENCY	NUMBER OF PETS
(5,2)	1	2
(5,4)	1	4
TOTAL	2	6

CATEGORY 7

DATA ITEM	FREQUENCY	NUMBER OF PETS
(6,4)	1	4
TOTAL	1	4

7 The last stage in the re-arrangement of the data items involves the construction of a final frequency table. This table summarizes all the totals and derived statistics in the previous 7 tables. It also contains a fourth column in which the derived statistics will be entered. In this table the totals from all the previous 7 tables are listed. In the next diagram this final frequency table is given with the first column filled in.

SUMMARY OF DATA ITEMS

Category	Number Of Households	Total Of Pets	Average Number Of Pets
1			
2			
3			
4			
5			
6			
7			

8 In the following diagram the second column has been filled in. The heading of the second column is 'Number of households' and this refers to the number of households in each Category. The numbers in this column are the totals under the 'Frequency' column in the previous tables. Check the numbers in this table against the appropriate numbers in the previous 7 tables to make sure you agree.

SUMMARY OF DATA ITEMS

Category	Number Of Households	Total Of Pets	Average Number Of Pets
1	45		
2	50		
3	70		
4	25		
5	7		
6	2		
7	1		

9 The third column contains the total number of pets in each Category of household. These numbers are the totals at the bottom of the third column of each of the previous 7 frequency tables. Check these numbers to make sure that you agree.

SUMMARY OF DATA ITEMS

Category	Number Of Households	Total Of Pets	Average Number Of Pets
1	45	36	
2	50	55	
3	70	126	
4	25	60	
5	7	21	
6	2	6	
7	1	4	

The final column consists of the AVERAGE number of pets in each category of household.

AVERAGE

10 The AVERAGE of a number of quantities is the sum of those quantities divided by the NUMBER of quantities. For example, the AVERAGE of the three numbers 4, 8 and 9 is the SUM $4 + 8 + 9 = 21$ divided by 3 - the NUMBER of numbers. So the AVERAGE is;

$$21 \div 3 = 7$$

Notice that the number 7 is not one of the numbers 4, 8 or 9. The AVERAGE is simply a number obtained by adding and dividing. It need not necessarily be one of the numbers added nor need it relate to reality. For example, if Joe had 15 marbles and Henry had 4 then the AVERAGE number of marbles possessed by Joe and Henry would be

$$(15+4) \div 2 = 9.5 \text{ each}$$

Obviously half a marble is of use to no-one but that is not the point. The average is simply a NUMBER obtained by adding and dividing.

11 The fourth column of the frequency table requires the entry of the average number of pets in each category of household. These entries are obtained by dividing the total number of pets in each category of household by the total number of households in that category. The numbers required are obtained by dividing the total pets given in the third column by the total households given in the second column. The first entry is then;

$$36 \div 45 = 0.8 \text{ pets per household}$$

The following diagram contains the frequency table with the fourth column filled in. Notice how all the numbers are neatly arranged in rows to make the table easy to read. Make sure that you agree with the numbers entered.

SUMMARY OF DATA ITEMS

Category	Number Of Households	Total Of Pets	Average Number Of Pets
1	45	36	0.8
2	50	55	1.1
3	70	126	1.8
4	25	60	2.4
5	7	21	3.0
6	2	6	3.0
7	1	4	4.0

THE ANSWER

12 From the frequency table it can be seen that as the category numbers increase in column one - that is as the number of children in a household increase, so the average number of pets in the household increase - shown in column four. The original question posed in this statistical enquiry, namely;

> **"Is the number of permanent pets in a household related in any way to the number of people 17 years old or younger in the same household on the Benevue Estate?"**

Can now be answered.

> **"From the data obtained it can be concluded that the average number of permanent pets in a household increases as the number of people 17 years old or younger increase in the same household on the Benevue Estate"**

COMMENTS ON THE ANSWER

13 The answer is very specific. It states exactly where the data was collected - the Benevue Estate. It also states exactly what is related - the permanent pets and the people 17 years old or younger in a household. Notice that it uses the word average. The final frequency table looked at averages and showed that the **average** number of pets in a household was related to the number of children in that household. **This is a very important point.** Whilst the general trend or behaviour may not be easily seen when looking at an individual that trend or behaviour may be very obvious when looking at a large group of individuals. For example, a single terrace spectator at a football match may be being jostled about in quite a random way but seen from the opposite terrace that spectator is just one of a whole mass of spectators that appear to be swaying rhythmically from side to side. Statistics is about the view from the opposite terrace. Statistics describes the group as a whole rather than the individual members of the group.

This completes the third part of the Statistical Enquiry. The final part, the communication of the results will be considered in the next Chapter.

SUMMARY

14 When data is originally collected it is rarely in a form suitable for deriving the statistics. The data must be re-arranged to put it into some form of order. Inspection of the data for common features allows the data to be grouped into CATEGORIES. Within each category data items may be repeated. The number of times a data item is repeated is called its FREQUENCY. Using categories and frequencies the data items can be re-arranged making it possible to construct a frequency table. The frequency table summarizes all the data items in a compact way.

When constructing a table the following points must be kept in mind;

1 All columns must be clearly separated by a vertical line.

2 Each column must be headed with a clear description of what it contains

3 The contents of the table must be entered in clearly defined rows.

4 The table must be clearly labelled to show what its contents refer to.

The AVERAGE is a very common statistic. The Average of a number of quantities is the sum of those quantities divided by the NUMBER of quantities.

The Answer to the question asked in a statistical enquiry must be precise and relate exactly to the question.

KEY POINTS TO NOTE

15 Re-arrangement of data. Categories. Frequency. Frequency table. Table construction. Average. Answering the question.

STUDENT SELF TESTING

SELF REVIEW EXERCISES

1 After data has been collected, why must it be re-arranged?(2,3)

2 What is a category?(3)

3 What is meant by the word 'frequency' when applied to data items?(4)

4 What is a frequency table? (5)

5 What four basic rules are to be applied when constructing a table?(5)

6 What is an average?(10)

7 How does the answer to a statistical enquiry relate to the question?(13)

EXERCISES (Answers begin on Page 249)

1. A Company manufactures electrical fuses and packs them into boxes of 10, 25, 50 and 100. From one day's production 12 boxes were selected and the fuses contained in them were tested. The following data items represent the result of the testing;

(10,1) ; (25,1) ; (100,6) ; (25,1) ; (10,0) ; (25,2) ; (50,2) ; (25,0) ; (10,1)
(10,0) ; (25,2) ; (100,2)

In each pair the first number represents the number of fuses in a particular box. The second number represents the number of defective fuses in the box.

        a) Re-arrange these data items into Categories

        b) Construct a frequency table for each Category

        c) Summarize the data items in a single table

        d) Is the number of fuses packed in a box related to the number of defective fuses in that box?

2. A single die was rolled 60 times. Each roll was recorded and the following table contains the complete record;

```
1 2 6 1 4 3 6 4 1 3
1 1 5 6 5 1 5 2 5 2
4 3 1 3 1 4 3 5 6 4
1 6 4 4 2 6 2 4 1 5
2 1 3 1 5 1 2 6 3 2
3 6 1 5 2 4 5 6 1 3
```

a) Construct a frequency table for this data

b) What is the average number rolled?

c) Is the die fair?

5 Communicating The Results

INTRODUCTION

1 This Chapter covers the method used to communicate the results of the statistical enquiry described in the previous three chapters. The communication takes the form of a display that portrays the essential components of the investigation. The conclusions are given in two forms. The first is a written conclusion and the second is in the form of **SYMBOLS**.

There are two major parts to this Chapter. They are;

> Communicating the Results
> Symbols

COMMUNICATING THE RESULTS

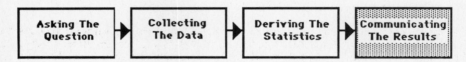

2 The purpose of communicating the results of a statistical enquiry is to display the findings to people who have not been involved in the enquiry. To convince such people that the results are accurate and reliable they must be able to verify them. The best way to do this is to give a brief synopsis of how the enquiry was carried out. In doing this care must be taken to ensure that the communication does not become cluttered with too much detail. Too much detail will detract from the essentials.

The Statistics teacher had arranged for a stall to be available at the school's Annual Open Day. The students were to be responsible for displaying their findings at this stall. To this end the students prepared a number of display cards.

3 Card 1 described the question asked in the enquiry. As a casual reader may not know what is meant by the phrase 'permanent pets' its definition is also included. Care must always be taken to define words that have a very specific meaning when communicating to the layman. Card 1 represents the first part of the statistical enquiry.

WEST LINTON HIGH SCHOOL
STATISTICS PROJECT

CARD 1 - THE QUESTION

The students of the Fourth Form recently carried out a Statistical Enquiry. They wished to know the answer to the following question;

Is the number of permanent pets in a household related in any way to the number of people 17 years old or younger in the same household on the Benevue Estate?

Definition of Permanent Pet - A pet that is expected to be kept in the household until it died naturally

4 The second card displayed the questionnaire and briefy described the people to whom it was distributed. It is necessary that the section of the population to whom the results apply is clearly identified. This ensures, for example, that the results applying to the people on the Benevue Estate are not assumed to apply to the entire population of the town or country.

WEST LINTON HIGH SCHOOL
STATISTICS PROJECT

CARD 2 - THE QUESTIONNAIRE

To find the answer to the question on Card 1 information had to be obtained from the households on the Benevue Estate. This was obtained by means of the following questionnaire. Every household on the Estate was given a copy to fill in. Of the 204 questionnaires distributed 200 were returned completed.

West Linton High School
39 Highway Road
Linton   **5 June**

On the 8th July the West Linton High School will be holding its Annual Open Day. This year the students of the Fourth Form have decided to perform a Statistical Enquiry and to display their findings at the Open Day.

Your cooperation in the enquiry is vital and the class would greatly appreciate your answers to the questions listed below. Your name and address will not be recorded against your replies so complete confidentiality is assured.

The question the class wishes to answer is;

> "Is the number of permanent pets in a household related in any way to the number of people 17 years old or younger in the same household on the Benevue Estate?"

To enable the students to solve this problem please answer the following questions;

1. How many people 17 years old or younger live in your house?
   _____

2. How many permanent pets live in your house? _____
   (A permanent pet is any living creature that you call a pet that is expected to
   live with you until it dies naturally. This does not include temporary pets such
   as litters of offspring that will be disposed of)

In anticipation of your cooperation the class would like to thank you. You are cordially invited to the Annual Open Day
to view their conclusions.

THIS QUESTIONNAIRE WILL BE COLLECTED BETWEEN 7 pm AND 8 pm NEXT MONDAY

5 The first two Cards adequately covered the first two parts of the Statistical Enquiry. The next
aspect to be dealt with was the third part of the Enquiry - deriving the statistics. The problem here
was to decide what to include and what to omit. Too many tables would clutter the display. Too few
would not convey enough information to make the display effective. It was decided to use two
Cards. The first Card would display the data items obtained from the questionnaires. The second
Card would display the final frequency table. Displaying the original data items and the final set of
numbers derived from the data items was sufficient.

WEST LINTON HIGH SCHOOL
STATISTICS PROJECT

CARD 3 - THE DATA

The following sets of pairs of numbers were created from the answers to the questionnaires. Each
pair of numbers represents one completed questionnaire. The first number in a pair is the number of
people 17 years old or younger in the household. The second number is the number of permanent
pets in that household.

```
( 0 , 1 ),( 0 , 1 ),( 0 , 2 ),( 1 , 0 ),( 1 , 3 ),( 1 , 0 ),( 0 , 2 )
( 2 , 1 ),( 0 , 0 ),( 0 , 2 ),( 2 , 2 ),( 1 , 3 ),( 0 , 0 ),( 0 , 1 )
( 4 , 5 ),( 2 , 1 ),( 0 , 0 ),( 0 , 0 ),( 3 , 2 ),( 2 , 1 ),( 2 , 3 )
( 2 , 3 ),( 3 , 2 ),( 2 , 3 ),( 2 , 2 ),( 4 , 2 ),( 1 , 0 ),( 2 , 1 )
( Ø , Ø ),( 3 , 2 ),( 2 , 2 ),( 3 , 3 ),( 1 , 1 ),( 0 , 2 ),( 1 , 2 )
( 2 , 2 ),( 2 , 2 ),( 2 , 2 ),( 1 , 0 ),( 2 , 1 ),( 2 , 3 ),( 3 , 3 )
-------------------------------------------------------------------------
( 3 , 1 ),( 1 , 1 ),( 0 , 0 ),( 1 , 1 ),( 0 , 0 ),( 0 , 1 ),( 2 , 1 )
( 2 , 2 ),( 1 , 2 ),( 2 , 1 ),( 5 , 4 ),( - , - ),( 3 , 3 ),( 0 , 1 )
( 1 , 1 ),( 3 , 3 ),( 1 , 2 ),( 2 , 1 ),( 2 , 1 ),( 3 , 3 ),( 2 , 3 )
( 0 , 0 ),( 2 , 2 ),( 2 , 2 ),( 2 , 2 ),( 2 , 3 ),( 1 , 0 ),( 1 , 1 )
( 2 , 2 ),( 1 , 1 ),( 1 , 3 ),( 3 , 3 ),( 3 , 3 ),( 2 , 2 ),( 2 , 2 )
( 0 , 0 ),( 2 , 4 ),( 1 , 2 ),( 2 , 1 ),( 0 , 0 ),( 2 , 1 ),( 2 , 2 )
```

```
-----------------------------------------------------------------
( 3 ,1 ),( 2 ,1 ),( 1 ,0 ),( 2 ,1 ),( 2 ,1 ),( 2 ,2 ),( 1 ,0 )
( 1 ,1 ),( 2 ,2 ),( 0, 1 ),( 2 ,1 ),( 0 ,2 ),( 1 ,1 ),( 2 ,1 )
( 0 ,1 ),( 0 ,1 ),( 0 ,1 ),( 0 ,0 ),( 2 ,3 ),( 3 ,3 ),( 2 ,3 )
( 2 ,1 ),( 2 ,1 ),( 3 ,3 ),( 0 ,1 ),( 1 ,1 ),( 2 ,4 ),( 1 ,0 )
( 0 ,0 ),( 1 ,2 ),( 2 ,3 ),( 2 ,0 ),( 3 ,3 ),( 1 ,2 ),( 3 ,2 )
( 1 ,2 ),( 1 ,0 ),( 2 ,1 ),( 2 ,3 ),( 2 ,2 ),( 1 ,2 ),( 2 ,1 )
-----------------------------------------------------------------
( 6 ,4 ),( - ,- ),( 0 ,2 ),( 0 ,0 ),( 0 ,0 ),( 2 ,2 ),( 0 ,0 )
( 1 ,3 ),( 0 ,2 ),( 0 ,0 ),( 3 ,3 ),( 1 ,0 ),( 4 ,4 ),( 0 ,1 )
( 1 ,0 ),( 2 ,2 ),( 4 ,0 ),( 1 ,0 ),( 1 ,0 ),( 2 ,2 ),( 1 ,3 )
( 3 ,1 ),( 2 ,1 ),( 1 ,0 ),( 0 ,1 ),( 1 ,2 ),( 0 ,2 ),( 2 ,1 )
( 3 ,2 ),( 2 ,3 ),( 3 ,3 ),( - ,- ),( 2 ,1 ),( 2 ,2 ),( 0 ,0 )
( 1 ,1 ),( 1 ,3 ),( 1 ,1 ),( 3 ,1 ),( 3 ,2 ),( 0 ,1 ),( 1 ,0 )
-----------------------------------------------------------------
( 0 ,1 ),( 2 ,1 ),( 0 ,1 ),( 2 ,1 ),( 1 ,1 ),( 2 ,2 )
( 2 ,2 ),( 2 ,1 ),( 1 ,0 ),( 5 ,2 ),( 1 ,0 ),( 2 ,1 )
( 0 ,1 ),( 4 ,4 ),( 0 ,1 ),( 0 ,0 ),( 1 ,1 ),( 0 ,2 )
( 2 ,3 ),( 2 ,3 ),( 1 ,2 ),( 0 ,1 ),( 1 ,3 ),( 1 ,1 )
( 3 ,3 ),( 2 ,1 ),( 1 ,0 ),( 0 ,0 ),( 2 ,1 ),( 3 ,2 )
( 1 ,0 ),( 2 ,2 ),( 3 ,3 ),( 2 ,2 ),( 0 ,1 ),( 4 ,4 )
-----------------------------------------------------------------
```

The entries (- , -) represent questionnaires that were not completed.

6 In the frequency table the first and the fourth columns were shaded to indicate that these two columns were the important ones. It is from these two columns that the conclusions were deduced. Also included in Card 4 would be a description of what the word `category' refers to. Again, this is a special word that has to be explained.

WEST LINTON HIGH SCHOOL
STATISTICS PROJECT

CARD 4 - SUMMARY OF THE INFORMATION OBTAINED

The answers to the questions on the questionnaire were analysed and the following Table is a summary of the information obtained.

SUMMARY OF DATA ITEMS

Category	Number Of Households	Total Of Pets	Average Number Of Pets
1	45	36	0.8
2	50	55	1.1
3	70	126	1.8
4	25	60	2.4
5	7	21	3.0
6	2	6	3.0
7	1	4	4.0

The households on the Benevue Estate were placed in categories. Category 1 consists of those households with no persons 17 years old or younger, category 2 consists of those households with one person 17 years old or younger. This process continues up to category 7 which consists of those household with 6 people 17 years old or younger.

7 The fifth Card described how the Table on Card 4 was read in order to form the conclusions. The conclusions were then given. Notice that these conclusions are identical to those given in paragraph 12 of Chapter 4 with the exception that the word **data** has been replaced with the word **information.** The word 'data' has a defined meaning as seen from paragraph 6 of Chapter 1. To avoid having to define the word 'data' the general word 'information' was substituted. As mentioned earlier, care must always be taken to either define words that have a very specific meaning or to avoid them when communicating to the layman.

WEST LINTON HIGH SCHOOL
STATISTICS PROJECT

CARD 5 - CONCLUSIONS (1)

Card 4 shows that as the numbers in column one increase so the numbers in column four increase. The numbers in column one relate to the number of people in a household who are 17 years old or younger. The numbers in column four relate to the average number of pets in each category of household. This is summarized in the following table;

Number Of People 17 Years Old Or Younger	Average Number Of Permanent Pets
0	0.8
1	1.1
2	1.8
3	2.4
4	3.0
5	3.0
6	4.0

From this table it can be seen that the answer to the question on Card 1 is;

From the information obtained it can be concluded that the average number of permanent pets in a household increases as the number of people 17 years old or younger increase in the same household on the Benevue Estate.

SYMBOLS

8 A good method of presenting results is in the form of pictures. Pictures can convey information more effectively than the written word. The pictures commonly used to illustrate the results of statistical enquiries are composed of SYMBOLS. Each symbol is a small shape that represents a particular idea. The most well known symbols are probably the outline drawings that distinguish the Ladies from the Gentleman's toilets. Whenever symbols are used to create a picture the picture must be accompanied by a KEY. A KEY is a list of the symbols used accompanied by their meanings.

The final Card the students prepared was a symbolic picture of their findings. The picture was accompanied by a KEY.

**WEST LINTON HIGH SCHOOL
STATISTICS PROJECT**

CARD 6 - CONCLUSIONS (2)

PEOPLE IN HOUSEHOLD   PERMANENT PETS

KEY

REPRESENTS ONE PERSON 17 YEARS OLD OR YOUNGER

REPRESENTS ONE PERMANENT PET

REPRESENTS NO PERSONS 17 YEARS OLD OR YOUNGER

9 To complete the contents of the stall the completed questionnaires were on display. These were available to anyone who wished to check the findings for themselves.

SUMMARY

10 The results of a statistical enquiry must be capable of being verified. For this reason the students displayed not only their conclusions but also a brief description of how they arrived at those conclusions. To achieve this the students prepared a number of Cards for their stall at the school's Annual Open Day. The four parts of the Statistical Enquiry were represented as follows;

Card 1   **The Question :**   Including a definition of the special term 'permanent pets'

Card 2   **The Questionnaire** : Including a description of the people who filled it in

Card 3   **The Data** : Including a description of how the data items were constructed.

Card 4   **Summary Of Information Obtained** : Including a description of the special term 'category'

Card 5   **Conclusions (1)** : Containing a written description of the conclusions and how the evidence supports them.

Card 6   **Conclusions (2)** : A symbolic display of the conclusions.

Also at the stall were the completed questionnaires. These were available to anyone who might wish to check the numbers.

KEY POINTS TO NOTE

11 The communication of results should permit verification. Too much detail can confuse the communication. Symbols and Key.

STUDENT SELF TESTING

SELF REVIEW EXERCISES

1 What is the purpose of communicating results? (2)

2 How are the results best communicated? (2)

3 Why must the population to whom the results refer be clearly identified when communicating the results (4)

4 Why is it not best to include every detailed calculation in a display of results? (2,5)

5 Why must special terms be defined? (6,7)

6 What is a symbol? (8)

7 What is the Key to a symbol picture? (8)

8 Should the evidence of a Statistical Enquiry be made generally available? Why? (9)

EXERCISES (Answers begin on Page 249)

1. The number of taxis in a railway station taxi-rank and the average waiting time were recorded on a number of occasions. The results are;

Waiting Time and Availability of Taxis

Number Of Taxis	2	3	4	5	6	7
Average Waiting Time (mins)	20	15	10	8	6	4

Draw a symbol picture to illustrate this data.

2. A building company has been investigating complaints received from the occupants of new buildings. Of 2000 recent complaints, 400 were about structural faults, 300 about plumbing faults, 700 about electrical faults and the remainder were about other types of fault.

800 complaints related to flats, 500 to bungalows and the remainder related to houses. Of the complaints about structural faults, half related to flats, and one quarter to houses. Of the complaints about plumbing faults, half related to houses and one third to flats. Of the complaints about electrical faults, one quarter related to bungalows and one quarter related to houses.

a) Construct a suitable table to display this information

b) Construct a symbolic picture to illustrate the distribution of type of fault (ie structural etc) of all new buildings.

LCCI 1986

Section 2   Asking Questions

This Section deals with the role of questions in a statistical enquiry. This role is considered from both an historical and a contemporary viewpoint. The correct and incorrect ways of posing questions are reviewed and the construction of a questionnaire is dealt with in depth.

There are six Chapters in this Section. They are;

1 Questions And Statistics

INTRODUCTION

1 This Chapter deals with the role of the question within our daily lives. It is shown that mankind's continual search for answers has been the motivation to develop Statistics. The need for Statistics is considered and the two types of Statistics, descriptive and inferential, are contrasted.

There are five major parts to this Chapter. They are;

> **Questions**
> **Foundations**
> **Need For Statistics**
> **Types Of Statistics**
> **The Need To Know**

QUESTIONS

2 Questions, Questions, Questions! Sometimes it seems that life consists of nothing but questions.

> When shall I get up?
> What shall I have for breakfast?
> At what time do I have to get to work?
> Will I have enough time to buy a newspaper?

And so the day progresses. Some questions are easily answered, others are more complicated. Deciding what to have for breakfast is a matter of desire. Deciding if you have enough time to buy a newspaper on the way to work is more involved - it requires other questions to be answered first.

> What is the time now?
> When is the next bus to work?
> How long will it take to nip into the newsagents?
> Will there be a queue?

Ordinarily we go through these question and answer sessions automatically but occasionally answers have to be found by conciously seeking for them. If you buy your newspaper and miss your bus you must search the timetable to find out when the next bus is due. This facility to fill our lives with questions has enabled us to progress from the primitive cave-dweller society of a few thousand years ago to the highly organized, technical society of today.

The Past

3 We are where we are today because questions have been asked and answered in the past. The Parthenon in Athens was constructed some 2,500 years ago using highly developed architectural skills. Those skills had been acquired over the ages by asking questions. How heavy is the roof going to be? How many pillars are going to be needed to hold it up? It was natural then to ask; How can we reduce the number of pillars? Seeking an answer to this question led to the invention of the arch.

The Present

4 We need to continually ask questions to cope with our daily lives. How much tax must the Government raise to pay for the Educational System, The Health Service or the Defence of the Country? How much fertilizer is needed per acre of land to ensure a healthy crop? If you were in the business of selling fish and chips you would need to know how much food to prepare to satisfy your customers. If you only start frying fish at lunchtime you will probably have a long queue of hungry customers waiting for the food to cook. By the time it was cooked many of them would have eaten elsewhere leaving you with a large number of congealing fried fish and chips. Not a good idea. You must ask questions about numbers of customers expected to arrive at a given time in the day and guage your operations according to the answers you come up with. This will involve past experience and prediction - a typical statistical exercise. Without performing this exercise you would lose money.

The Future

5 If we are to have any future at all there are many questions that must be answered, if not now then in the future. Where is the world to obtain its fuel when the oil and coal have all been used? The need to know the answer to that question may lie in the future but the future will come and the answer will be needed.

6 So many of the questions that we ask ourselves can only be answered by using ARITHMETIC. How many pillars? How many customers? How much coal and oil? All of Statistics is based upon Arithmetic. Without Arithmetic there would be no Statistics. However, Statistics is more than just Arithmetic. Statistics involves many other processes that we shall learn about but without Arithmetic the Statistical Method would not exist.

FOUNDATIONS

7 The Foundation of the statistical process is Arithmetic - the manipulation of numbers using the four rules of addition, subtraction, multiplication and division.

8 Arithmetic had its beginnings many thousands of years ago when primitive man found a need to count and to estimate his needs. How much wood do I need to keep this fire alight all night? To be able to answer questions such as this was necessary for survival. Whilst Arithmetic had its origins in the humble environment of the cave its development into a sophisticated calculating system was driven by more elaborate schemes. When the Pharoes of ancient Egypt demanded the Pyramids be built some 3000 years ago their architects had to use Statistics to estimate the amounts of labour and materials required. They had to ask questions relating to the location of the Pyramid, the size of the Pyramid, the details of the burial chamber and many other aspects of its construction.

9 The Kings of ancient Babylon knew that a certain portion of each year's harvest had to be set aside to see the populace through the lean years of drought and pestilence. This planning required the use of Statistics.

10 Twenty years after the Norman invasion of England in 1066 William the Conqueror ordered a massive statistical enquiry be undertaken. He ordered that every landholding in his kingdom be listed and described - what taxes were due, how many plough teams there were, how much property the land supported and so on. All this information was recorded in the Domesday Book - so called because of its ultimate authority on the settlement of disputes concerning land rights.

11 Statistical Exercises such as these involved large numbers of people and cost huge amounts of money. The only people who could afford to mount such ventures were those with access to wealth - the rulers of nations. Indeed, the word STATISTICS is derived from the phrase STATE ARITHMETIC.

12 In eighteenth century England the Industrial Revolution created wealth where hitherto there had been none. The owners of factories could afford to mount their own statistical enquiries. They needed answers to such questions as;

> At what age is a person physically capable of starting to work full time?

> How will education affect my workforce?

> How many hours can a weaving machine be expected to operate before it needs repair?

> How many workers will be need to manufacture a steam engine in a week?

> How much money is needed to build a mill?

> How much cash needs to be drawn from the Bank to pay the weekly wages?

13 The desire to answer questions such as these promoted further developments in the statistical methods. The more elaborate and involved the questions became so the more involved and elaborate the arithmetic and hence the statistics had to become. Indeed, Industry and Commerce have been responsible for much statistical development to the present day.

NEED FOR STATISTICS

14 Statistics are needed for two reasons. Firstly, statistics are needed to evaluate the present state of affairs and to put them into historical perspective. The teacher who has examined his students will want to know what the average mark of the class is. This will give the present state of affairs. By comparing this year's average mark with the average marks of previous years the teacher will be able to judge the merits of this year's class with those of previous years. This will put this year's average mark into historical perspective. Statistics that answer questions of this sort are called DESCRIPTIVE STATISTICS.

15 Secondly, statistics are needed to predict the future course of events and to allow planning to anticipate such future expectations. For example, a governing political party will commission a popularity poll to determine how popular it is and to predict whether or not they would win an election held in the near future. This is the prediction of the future course of events. Having made the prediction the party will then decide whether or not to hold an election. This is the plan to anticipate future expectation. Statistics that answer questions of this sort are called INFERENTIAL STATISTICS - they INFER the future.

TYPES OF STATISTICS

16 As we saw in the last section there are two types of Statistics

> **Descriptive Statistics**
> **Inferential Statistics**

DESCRIPTIVE STATISTICS

17 Descriptive Statistics are just what their name suggests. They are statistics that DESCRIBE the actual state of a situation as it exists now or as it existed in the past. Every car has a display of the total mileage it has travelled since it was new. This display of total mileage is a statistic that describes the present state of how much the car has been used. As a further example, in 1970 there were some 200 million people living in the USA. This total population is a statistic that describes the past state of the USA's population. What cannot be measured, of course, is something that has not yet happened. Descriptive Statistics do not describe the future. The role of describing the future is left to inferential statistics.

INFERENTIAL STATISTICS

18 Inferential statisitcs INFER the future from a record of the past and present. The agricultural chemist who is studying the effect of a certain pesticide on a small plot of land will be able to deduce the effect when it is applied to a large acreage of farm land. He can infer the widespread effect from the results obtained in the laboratory environment.

THE NEED TO KNOW

19 There is an ever present need to know about the world around us. Governments need to know the answers to countless questions to enable them to govern. Corporations need to know the answers to questions to enable them to control their various departments and to retain viability. We as individuals need to know to enable us to live effectively. The only way the need to know can be satisfied is by asking questions.

SUMMARY

20 The facility for continually asking questions has enabled mankind to develop from the primitive cave society of yester-year to the highly stuctured and technically sophisticated society of today. Many questions can only be answered by using statistical methods. For this reason a highly developed discipline is necessary to answer many of today's questions.

Statistics is founded upon arithmetic and history teaches us that arithmetic has developed by necessity. Mankind has always found it necessary to predict and control the environment to enable it to survive. As a consequence, Statistics has developed into two basic forms. The first is descriptive statistics. By using descriptive statistics we can obtain some understanding of the world as it has developed and as it now exists. The second is inferential statistics. Based on an understanding of the world we can use inferential statistics to attempt to predict and thereby control future events. This is the ultimate goal of those who use inferential statistics - to influence the future.

KEY POINTS TO NOTE

21 Foundations of statistics, Need for statistics, Descriptive statistics, Inferential statistics.

STUDENT SELF TESTING

SELF REVIEW QUESTIONS

1. What are Descriptive Statistics? (14,17)

2. What are Inferential Statistics? (15,18)

EXERCISES (Answers begin on Page 249)

1. You are the ruler of a small, thriving state and you require money to maintain an army. Your sources of revenue consist of landowners, traders and manufacturers of a kind of pottery unique to your state. What questions must be answered before you can levy taxes that your subjects would consider to be fair?

2. A Company has a contract to build a bridge across a river between two towns. A bridge would save a journey of some 100 miles between these two towns. To build the bridge the Company will have to borrow a large amount of money from a bank. When the bridge is built the Company will obtain a return on its investment by levying a toll on the users of the bridge. What questions must be answered to ensure that the Company will make a profit over the ten year period following the construction of the bridge?

3. In each of the following three situations identify where descriptive and inferential statistics will have to be used.

a) Planning a coach trip to a theatre for an amateur dramatic group.

b) Shopping for the week's groceries.

c) Pricing home made jam for eventual sale in a local delicatessen.

2 Who Asks The Questions

INTRODUCTION

1 In this Chapter we illustrate the fact that questions arise in all walks of life. From our personal semi-structured daily life to highly organized and ultra-efficient organisations. We look briefly at the sort of questions asked by Government and Business Management.

There are four major parts to this Chapter. They are;

> **Daily Life**
> **Government**
> **Business Management**
> **Corporate Organisation**

DAILY LIFE

2 We all use statistical methods; many times without realizing it. If a car journey has to be made between Manchester and Leeds then a regular traveller of that route will have a rough idea of how long it will take. This estimate will be a result of accumulated experience that allows the traveller to give a reasonable guess of the expected time. Someone not used to this journey will measure the distance approximately by adding up a sequence of distances on a map from starting point to destination. Knowing how far one can travel in an hour they will then be able to estimate an expected journey time. Neither of these two times will be spot on but if they are accurate to ten or fifteen minutes they will be considered to be accurate enough. Such is the statistical approach. This is not to say that Statistics deals with rough approximations. Rather, it deals with a collection of data that is manipulated to arrive at some conclusion. In the first case the data consists of an accumulated experience of journeys and in the second case the data consists of a sequence of measurements.

3 There are numerous similar examples. Saving spending money for a holiday - one doesn't know exactly what is needed, a rough figure is sufficient provided it is above the obvious minimum when taking fares, food and accomodation into account.

4 A parent buying a pair of shoes for a child. Given the choice of a sturdy but expensive pair against a less sturdy but cheaper pair the question arises; Will the shoes wear out before the child grows out of them? Making such a decision as this is a statistical process involving past experience.

5 Buying food for a family for a week is a statistical process. If I buy a large jar of coffee it will last longer than a week. If I buy a small jar it will not be enough. So I buy a large jar this week and a small jar next week in the hope that after two weeks all will balance out. How much am I spending? How often do you see a shopper using a calculator? Not very often. Many people have a mental picture of an amount of money that gradually decreases as they pluck items off the supermarket shelves. They seem to know how much they can afford - the essence of a statistical process.

6 Time and again we all use statistical methods without conciously realizing it at the time. The youngster who must not step on a crack has to estimate a comparison between stride length and crack-free paving. One big step, two small steps,...... it's all statistics.

GOVERNMENT

7 The Government has a basic interest in statistics because that is the most important way it obtains information regarding what needs to be done, what is politically possible and what effect its policies have had. In this section we shall just consider the four areas of;

Education
Health Care
Crime
Science and Technology

There are obviously many other areas but space is limited and the four chosen are representative.

EDUCATION

8 The Government must first plan the number of schools required. This relates to the number of students and the acceptable class size. The number of students who will be a given age, say 11 years old, in 5 years time is already known. Government agencies have done their statistical analyses and know how many six year olds are alive today. From this they can guage how many 11 year olds will be around in 5 years time. Hence they plan the schools.

9 Every School requires teachers and equipment. Again these numbers are balanced against student numbers and the money available - a statistical exercise.

10 The curriculum must also be planned to meet the needs of the school leaver looking for employment. As the employment market changes so the needs of the school leaver changes. Since it takes time to plan a change in a curriculum those who do the planning must have sufficient foresight to make a reasonable prediction of the market needs some five or six years ahead. Not an easy task but one that must be done and done using statistics.

HEALTH CARE

11 From past experience and population trends the Government agencies are able to predict the amount of geriatric care required, the amount of emergency care expected and the general hospital admissions needs. From all this data they can conclude how many hospitals and clinics will be required and where they should be located. They can also budget for the staffing by Medics and Nurses, for the drugs and medicines used, for the specialist care facilities. All done by statistics.

CRIME

12 Crime is forever with us and an efficient and effective police force must be maintained to combat the criminal. Crime patterns are studied to predict how best to deploy the forces currently available and to predict how many additional forces will be required.

13 Coupled with this the Police have to be equipped - truncheons, cars, helmets, motorbikes, notepads, uniforms, guns. All these requirements are statistically estimated.

14 The Police themselves understand the best methods of patrolling, whether it be on foot or by car. Again based on past experience. The quantity of Police turned out during a particularly sensitive Football match is a demonstation of the statistical method predicting the quantity of Policemen required to control a crowd of potentially unruly youth.

SCIENCE AND TECHNOLOGY

15 The Government is responsible for promoting and financing many scientific projects within the ambit of Science and Technology. Medical research into new drugs, new treatments for old ailments. Energy research into new or more efficient methods of energy generation and new methods of energy conservation. Raw materials control - oil, gas, coal, forestry - all require statistical analysis to enable effective planning. Training via the Universities and Polytechnics bringing us back full cycle to Education.

16 The Public Libraries abound with Goverment Statistics. Why not stop reading this minute and go to your Public Library. If you go into the Reference Section and ask for a copy of the latest edition of Monthly Digest of Statistics the librarian will be only too delighted to assist you. In this publication you will see table upon table of statistics painstakingly gathered to help the Government to govern. This could also be an execellent opportunity to browse round the Statistics Section and discover the many publications there.

BUSINESS MANGEMENT

17 Commerce and Industry need Statistics to operate effectively. Here we shall consider just five specific activities where statistics are playing a vital role;

> **Production**
> **Stock Control**
> **Manpower**
> **Finance**
> **Sales and Advertising**

PRODUCTION

18 Statistical methods have to be used to balance supply against demand, develop the cheapest techniques and control the quality of the product. For example, if the testing of a unit meant that it was subsequently unsaleable then it would be foolhardy to test every unit that was made. Instead samples are chosen on a statistical basis and these samples tested. We shall say more about this in Chapter 2 of Section 3. Optimizing production also involves plant layout and location near a workforce within easy reach by local transport.

STOCK CONTROL

19 The purpose of keeping merchandise in stock is to have a ready supply on hand to avoid shortfalls. An inability to supply an advertised item can annoy customers and drive them to the competition. Consequently, a statistical analysis must be made of customer demand for a product to ensure that sufficient quantities are held in stock. However, it costs money to maintain a warehouse and to employ people to handle the stock. As a result one must not hold too much of any one product in stock as this will waste money. Balancing these two aspects of stock control - satisfying customers and keeping costs down - is a continuing process and calls heavily on statistical techniques.

MANPOWER

20 Enough personnel must be available to ensure the most efficient job is done but having too large a personnel would be financially wasteful. Again a balance is achieved statistically. Furthermore, manpower planning must estimate future needs and apply their findings to recruitment and training. The time-handling of personnel in terms of overtime or short-time requires a statistical plan related to production requirements which are themselves linked to order book requirements. In recent years the 'Fast Food Industry' has seen a widespread use of part-time employment. This requires statistical techniques to be used in man-management to control the staffing of an outlet that could be open as much as 18 hours a day.

FINANCE

21 Any Company that wishes to remain in business must keep a close watch on its cash flow. Money paid out should always be less than money brought in and maintaining a balance to avoid an overdraft can call upon deft statistical skills. Long range financial management must optimise a Company's future by trying to maximize revenue whilst at the same time trying to minimize costs.

SALES AND ADVERTISING

22 The Company must maintain an efficient sales force. This involves, amongst other things, making sure that the sales transport fleet is properly maintained. Regular servicing and replacing of vehicles is done on a statistical basis to reduce the fleet costs.

23 A Salesman must earn more for the Company than the Company pays him. As a result new markets must be continually investigated. Advertising must be appropriate and effective with surveys done to check that the advertising has had an effect.

24 Channels of communication within the Company have to be as efficient as possible. Is it worthwhile having a telephone in the car? Some salesmen, upon making a sale will enter the details into their portable computer and then by using their car telephone will transmit the information to their main computer at head office. This will then immediately create an order form, a despatch note, an invoice and automatically adjust the stock record. In fact by the time the salesman has said goodbye to his customer the goods could be practically on their way.

CORPORATE ORGANISATION

25 Every large corporate organisation uses committees to control and organise its various departments. The Government has its Cabinet and a Company has its Board of Directors. For the committees to operate effectively and efficiently they require information from all the departments that they control. If they oversee a large number of departments the total information they have to deal with can be immense. As a consequence this information has to be presented in a very condensed form. This again is dependent upon the Statistical Method. We shall see in the last section of this book how this is achieved. Suffice it to say here that answering questions is not the sole objective of Statistics. Those answers must be communicated and Statistics takes this aspect on board as well.

SUMMARY

26 Continual questioning demands that we all use statistics. In our personal lives we use statistics almost without realizing it. Many of the questions that we pose ourselves are too vague for precise answers and our estimation of the answer must naturally use statistics. The more important the question the more concious of the statistical method we have to be. Evidence for this lies in any highly stuctured organisation such as Government and Business Management. Both Government and Business Management consist of separate departments that not only deal with very complex problems individually but also work together as a coherent whole. The very nature of the questions they ask themselves are so involved that a highly developed statistical method is the only way of finding meaningful answers. Inter-departmental communication must be efficient. In an organisation with many departments this communication must be brief, informative and effective. This efficiency is achieved by the statistical method.

KEY POINTS TO NOTE

27 Questions in daily life, Government questions, Questions in business management, Corporate organisation

STUDENT SELF TESTING

SELF REVIEW QUESTIONS

1. What questions do you ask that require statistical answers? (2-6)

2. List 4 areas of Government that use statistics. (7)

3. List 5 areas of Business that use statistics. (17)

4. Why do Corporate committees demand the use of statistics? (26)

EXERCISES (Answers begin on Page 249)

1. You are planning a cycling holiday in a foreign country. What questions must be answered to ensure that your holiday is as successful and trouble-free as possible?

2. You own a small Company employing four people making stained glass windows. What questions should be continually answered to ensure that your Company remains successful and grows?

3 How to Ask Questions

INTRODUCTION

1 This Chapter deals with the correct way to pose problems and to ask the appropriate questions.

There are three major parts to this Chapter. They are;

> **Clearly Stated Problems**
> **Simple And Concise Questions**
> **Precise Answers**

CLEARLY STATED PROBLEMS

2 Before any questions can be phrased the problem under investigation must be closely analysed and clearly stated. It is imperative that the object of the exercise be clearly understood before designing the questions otherwise the questions asked may end up not being appropriate. For instance, we could ask the question

> **How many wheels does the average truck possess?**

This question poses a very unclear problem. Firstly, how do we decide what is a truck and what is not a truck? Should we decide by weight. For example,

> **A truck is any commercial vehicle that has an unladen weight of at least 3 tonnes.**

Having decided what a truck is we have still not completely, clarified this aspect of the question. What if the truck has a trailer, do we include this? Remember that a trailer could be the rear part of an articulated truck or it could be a coupled trailer. In Australia some trans-continental trucks can have as many as four coupled trailersd. Even if we include trailers of any variety we have still not completely clarified the problem. How do we define wheels? Many tucks have double wheels as well as single wheels. Do double wheels count as two wheels?

3 What is exemplified here is that the problem, to be clearly defined must be broken down into its elementary components. In this way questions can be asked relating to each component. There is no point in attempting to attack a problem as a single one when in fact it is a double one. For instance, in a problem involving people it must be clarified at the outset whether or not it is a problem involving men and women together or separately.

SIMPLE AND CONCISE QUESTIONS

4 Once the problem has been broken down into its component parts each part must be attacked individually. Each question must be simple and easily understood. If in doubt increase the number of questions. Two are better than one if in that way a point of confusion can be cleared up.

PRECISE ANSWERS

5 Questions must be phrased in such a way that they can be precisely answered. Imprecise questions lead to imprecies answers which are of little or no use whatsoever. For example the question,

Do you approve of pets?

is an example of this. What is meant by approve? Does it mean do you like owning a pet? Does it mean you do not object to other people owning pets? What is meant by pet? I like dogs but I dislike caged birds yet both are considered as pets. There are four ways in which a question can be set to allow it to be answered with precision. These are questions with;

> **Yes or No Answers**
> **Precoded Answers**
> **Rating Scale Answers**
> **Open Ended Answers**

YES OR NO ANSWERS

6 Some questions have only one of two possible answers. In this case each option can be precise. For example,

Do you attend night classes YES/NO (delete which does not apply)

or

Please state sex MALE/FEMALE (delete which does not apply)

PRECODED ANSWERS

7 Some questions may have more than two possible answers but the possible answers are nonetheless known. In this situation the possible answers can be listed after the question and the respondant requested to place a tick alongside the answer appropriate to their case. For example,

How many pairs of shoes do you possess?

(a) Between 1 and 3 pairs ☐
(b) Between 4 and 6 pairs ☐
(c) 7 pairs or more ☐

Tick the appropriate box

RATING SCALE ANSWERS

8 Some questions neccessarily require imprecise answers especially when dealing with opinions. In an attempt to obtain some precision in the answers a rating scale can be given. For example,

Do you believe in Capital Punishment as a form of punishment?

(a) Strongly disbelieve ☐
(b) Mildly disbelieve ☐
(c) Am indifferent ☐
(d) Mildly believe ☐
(e) Strongly believe ☐

The person who responds to this question is still left with a problem to decide the difference between **Strongly** and **Mildly** but at least some form of measure has been attained. Another type of rating scale is a numerical one.

On a scale of 1 to 10 do you rate yourself as a patient person?

impatient   patient

1   2   3   4   5   6   7   8   9 10
☐ ☐ ☐ ☐ ☐ ☐ ☐ ☐ ☐ ☐

Place a tick on the scale

OPEN ENDED ANSWERS

9 There are of course questions that can be answered precisely but not predictably. In this case the question seeks an open-ended answer - one where the person responding is free to write the answer in a blank space provided. Questions which require this type of response are used when the questionner is looking for ideas and opinions. For example

Do you have any suggestions for improving your working conditions?

or
What are your views on Sunday Trading?

SUMMARY

10 Prior to asking questions the problem posed must be clearly stated. All vague terms must be eliminated and each part of the problem must be stated in its elemental form. The problem has to be fully understood so that the questions asked are appropriate.

The questions themselves must be simple, concise and capable of a precise answer. This latter can be achieved by using;

> **YES/NO Answers**
> **Prcoded Answers**
> **Rating Scale Answers**
> **Open Ended Answers.**

KEY POINTS TO NOTE

11 Clearly stated problems, Simple and concise questions, Precise answers

STUDENT SELF TESTING

SELF REVIEW QUESTIONS

1. What is must be done before a question is posed? (2,3)

2. How should a question be phrased? (4)

3. List 4 methods of obtaining precise answers. (5)

EXERCISES (Answers begin on Page 249)

1. In each of the following situations post the problem clearly and construct an appropriate question;

a) Find out the average number of papers sold by 10 newsagents.

b) Find out the average number of sheets of paper filled in by 30 students sitting an examination.

2. Decide which of the four methods of obtaining precise answers you would use for each of the following questions. Re-write each question in its appropriate form.

a) How many doors do you have in your home?

b) Do you cycle to work?

c) How do you rate your golfing skills?

d) Do you enjoy hiking?

e) What are your views on pollution from car exhaust fumes?

4 How Not To Ask Questions

INTRODUCTION

1 Not only is it important to be aware of how to ask questions it is equally important to be aware of the many pitfalls that can occur when designing questions. In this Chapter a list of Dont's is presented under the following headings;

> **Multiple Questions in One**
> **The Use Of Unfamiliar Words**
> **Questions Containing Multiple Instructions**
> **Questions Requiring Calculations**
> **Questions Relying On Memory**
> **Questions That Are Inappropriate**
> **Questions That Are Unnecessary**
> **Tactless or Offensive Questions**
> **Ambiguous Questions**
> **Biased Questions**

MULTIPLE QUESTIONS IN ONE

2 Multiple questions occur when the questionner uses the joining words **AND** and **OR**.

> **Do You smoke and drink alcohol?**

You may drink alcohol but not smoke, equally you may smoke and not drink alcohol. In either case you should logically answer no to this question. However, in doing so the respondent would probably feel uneasy having the impression that this is not what the questionner meant. Again,

> **Do you go to work by bus or by car?**

It depends, sometimes bus, sometimes car. Though there is less confusion here it can still raise doubts in the mind of the respondent. The art of the good question is displayed when the questionners intent is absolutely clear. The respondent should never be left in the position wondering what exactly the questionner meant by a question or how it should be answered.

THE USE OF UNFAMILIAR WORDS

3 It is essential that the question be phrased in plain English using commonly used words. For example

> **Do you think that banning the sale of fireworks to persons under the age of
> 18 would ameliorate the problem of accidental burns on Bonfire Night?**

That word **ameliorate** would probably cause a dash for the dictionary. There is nothing wrong with the use of the word, it is just not a commonly used word and may not be immediately understood by a sizeable proportion of the respondants.

Jargon must also be avoided - it is usually understood only by those people who habitually use it. For example,

> **Do your debits exceed your credits?**

This question may be fine for accountants but for the ordinary man-in-the-street it could be better phrased as,

> **Do you owe more than is owed you?**

Abbreviations must likewise be avoided or at the very least explained.

> **Do you approve of VAT (Value Added Tax) being charged on children's clothes?**

Maybe everyone knows what **VAT** is but even so the habit of explaining abbreviations and initials such as these is a good habit to get into.

4 Be careful that the question does not include an invented word. English is a very flexible language in that words can be invented and by their very nature are capable of conveying meaning. For example, a **workstation** is word that was coined to mean a **desk with a computer on it**. If you have never heard the word before, you may miss the exact meaning but a meaning would have been imparted such as **a place of work**. Again, this can be avoided by the use of plain English.

QUESTIONS CONTAINING MULTIPLE INSTRUCTIONS

5 This type of question can cause confusion in the mind of the respondent thereby resulting in unreliable answers - such answers being worth little. For example,

> **Enter the number at the top left hand corner of this form and indicate in the space below it if this is larger than or smaller than your previous week's tax code.**

QUESTIONS REQUIRING CALCULATIONS

6 These can be very inaccurately answered especially if there is more than one way to perform the calculation. For example,

> **How much do you spend on electricity in a week?**

Usually bills are sent every three months. How many weeks are there in three months? It depends upon the particular three months - sometimes it is about 12 with a few days left over and sometimes about 13 with a few days left over. Also a winter week would require more electricity than a summer week. The answers to this question can not be expected to be very accurate. Even if the calculation is straightforward there is still a possibility that it will be incorrectly performed.

QUESTIONS RELYING ON MEMORY

How many times a year do you have your haircut?

7 Unless you are the sort of person who has their hair cut regularly or keeps a diary in which you record such momentous events as haircuts then the chances are that you cannot answer this question at all accurately.

How many light bulbs did you use in the last six months?

Again, can you remeber the exact last three times you replaced a light bulb? It would be far better to have asked;

When you buy light bulbs do you buy them?

(a) **Singly** ☐
(b) **In pairs** ☐
(c) **More than two at a time** ☐

How often do you buy light bulbs?

(a) **Each week** ☐
(b) **Each month** ☐
(c) **Other (please specify)** ☐ _____

In this way a more reliable result can be divined from the responses.

QUESTIONS THAT ARE INAPPROPRIATE

8 It is bad enough being asked to answer questions without being asked to answer questions that are irrelevant to the enquiry. For example, in a list of questions dealing with consumer tastes a question asking whether you own or rent your home would be totally out of place and inapproriate.

QUESTIONS THAT ARE UNECCESSARY

9 The date of Birth and Age are two questions that are frequently asked together yet only one of them is necessary.

TACTLESS OR OFFENSIVE QUESTIONS

10 Questions that are likely to offend should not be asked. For example,

> **How did you vote in the last Election?**

is tactless and some people would feel entitled to take offence. The vote is, after all, a secret ballot. Some questions can cause offence among certain sectors of the population generally because of tactless phrasing. For example, The use of the masculine gender can offend some women. It is very little extra trouble to use His/Her instead of just His.

AMBIGUOUS QUESTIONS

11 Questions must be capable of only one interpretation. If there are two or more interpretations possible then there are in effect two or more questions being answered. For example,

> **Do you think electric fires are better than gas fires?**

What is meant by **better**? Does it mean **cheaper**? Does it mean **cleaner**? Does it mean **more efficient**? What does it mean?

BIASED QUESTIONS

12 A biased question is a dishonest question. If a biased question is answered thoughtlessly then it is possible for the answers to be led in a specific direction by the question itself. This can be done by;

> **Asking leading questions**
> **Using emotional words**

ASKING LEADING QUESTIONS

13 A leading question begs a specific answer. For example,

> **Do you not think that Nuclear Weapons prevent war?**

The use of the negative **not** makes it very dificult to answer 'no' to this question because the question is phrased to expect a 'yes'. This ploy is sometimes used by lawyers in a court of law and looked upon very unkindly by a watchful Judge.

USE OF EMOTIONAL WORDS

14 Questions and answers should be as objective as possible.

> **Do you think it right to kill an unborn child by abortion?**

Such emotional phrasing can hardly be answered with a bald 'yes'. This sort of questioning is nothing short of downright dishonest. It is questioning and perpetrating an opinion at the same time.

SUMMARY

15 It is easier to ask a bad question than a good one. A good question requires care to enable it to be properly constructed. Two familiar traps to avoid falling into are asking multiple questions in one and using unfamiliar words. To avoid the first, break all questions down into their component parts and make sure that each part only asks one question. To avoid the second, always use simple words. Avoid jargon and new words that are currently popular. Good questions also avoid instructions, calculations and a reliance on memory. Above all be honest. Make sure that your questions do not force one answer in favour of another - avoid bias.

KEY POINTS TO NOTE

16 Multiple questions in one, Unfamiliar words, Instructions, Calculations, Memory, Bias, Leading questions, Emotional words

STUDENT SELF TESTING

SELF REVIEW QUESTIONS

1. How are multiple questions avoided? (2)

2. How are abbreviations handled? (3)

3. Why must questions avoid multiple instructions? (5)

4. Why must questions not require calculations? (6)

5. Why must a question not rely on the respondant's memory? (7)

6. What is an ambiguous question? (11)

7. List 2 types of biased question. (12)

EXERCISE (Answers begin on Page 249)

Find the flaws in each of the following questions. Re-phrase them to avoid the flaws.

1 Do you like cats and dogs?

2 How much PAYE do you pay each week?

3 Do you not agree that football hooligans should be dealt with more severely?

4 How much alcohol do you drink in a week?

5 Do you read?

6 Do you take much exercise in the week?

7 Do you eat healthy food?

5 Questionnaire Design

INTRODUCTION

1 All students of Statistics should understand the basic principles of questionnaire construction. In this Chapter these principles are discussed.

There are four major sections to this Chapter. They are;

> **The Purpose of a Questionnaire**
> **Constructing Questionnaires**
> **Distribution and Collection**

THE PURPOSE OF A QUESTIONNAIRE

2 A questionnaire is simply a list of questions and its purpose is to obtain information from a group of people by asking each person the same set of questions. The information so gathered could be kept in its original form on a card index file or it could be used as a basis for a statistical enquiry. For example, a questionnaire on a card could be used to store the details of each employee in a Company. The questionnaire, when completed, would then be kept in this form and filed away for future reference - this is the card index file. On the other hand a questionnaire consisting of questions on customer appreciation of a particular product could be used to measure the general public response to the product.

Whatever the questionnaire is for it still presents a respondant, the person who answers the questions, with a list of questions. As such it is an imposition and requires the goodwill of the respondant for its success. For this reason we must take care to construct the questionnaire according to the well defined rules that are laid out here.

CONSTRUCTING QUESTIONNAIRES

3 Every questionnaire is sub-divided into sections. Each section should be isolated from the other sections. This can be achieved by enclosing each section within a box. We shall consider the following questionnaire sections;

> **Object and Authority**
> **Instructions**
> **Details of Respondant**
> **The Body of The Enquiry**

OBJECT AND AUTHORITY

4 Every questionnaire is created for a reason. This reason, the OBJECT of the the enquiry must be clearly stated at the very beginning of the first section of the questionnaire. The respondant must be in no doubt about the reasons for requesting the information. This will probably take the form of WHAT THE ENQUIRY IS TRYING TO ESTABLISH and WHY IT IS TRYING TO ESTABLISH IT. For example

> **This questionnaire is trying to establish the extent to which the recent influenza virus has spread within this area. From the results of this Statistical Enquiry it will be decided whether or not to institute a free vaccine service starting next Winter.**

The people or the Institution who are responsible for the questionnaire, the AUTHORITY, must also be clearly shown giving name, address, post code and telephone number. This will then permit the respondant to contact the perpetrators and to check their intentions. For example,

This questionnaire is issued by;

> **The League Of Animal Friends**
> **123, High Street**
> **Lowtown LT1 2HS**
> **Tel (0123) 567890**

5 Finally in this section, don't forget you are relying on the respondants goodwill , so remember to thank the respondant and, if possible, indicate when and where the results of the enquiry will be available for viewing.

INSTRUCTIONS

6 The second section of the questionnaire should contain the INSTRUCTIONS and these will instruct the respondant;

> **How To Complete**
> **When To Complete**
> **How To Return The Questionnaire**

HOW TO COMPLETE

7 There may be a need for special instructions such as using a pen, or printing to ensure legibility. If the questionnaire is to be read by a computer it may be necessary to request that the questionnaire be completed in a special pencil provided for the purpose. If the respondant is blind then it may be necessary to have the form filled in by someone else on their behalf in which case this should be made clear.

WHEN TO COMPLETE

8 It may be that the perpetrators of the questionnaire wish the form to be filled in at a specific time or within a specific period of time. At all events, the latest time for the completion of the questionnaire should be given.

HOW TO RETURN THE QUESTIONNAIRE

9 If the questionnaire is to be collected then the date and time of collection should be iuncluded in this section. If the questionnaire is to be returned by post this information should also be given. In the latter case a post-paid, addresssed envelope ahould be included with the questionnaire. there is no reason why the respondant should incur any costs, however minimal. In all cases the instructions should be both CLEAR AND CONCISE and FEW IN NUMBER.

DETAILS OF THE RESPONDANT

10 The respondant is the person who responds to the questionnaire by answering the questions. Should the questionnaire require personal details these should be confined to name, age, address, occupation and other relevant questions. Some questionnaires, such as medical questionnaires will necessarily request personal details in the body of the enquiry. In all cases the nature of personal questions can be a sensitive area of enquiry and the confidentiality of the respondant must be assured at all times. Remember the points noted in the previous Chapter regarding question design. Such details about the respondant should only be requested if essential to the enquiry.

BODY OF THE ENQUIRY

11 The set of questions that form the main body of the enquiry must be clearly set apart from the remainder of the questionnaire. The following points must then be noted;

> **Points previously noted**
> **Length Of Questions**
> **Sequence Of Questions**
> **Units To Be Used In Answers**

POINTS PREVIOUSLY NOTED

12 Consider all the points raised in the previous Chapter concerning the design of questions

LENGTH OF QUESTIONS

13 Questions should not be too long. Extended questions can be confusing so the secret is to be concise yet at the same time clear in meaning. Where possible, try to confine each question to a single line or part line with sufficient space to the right of it to allow the answer to be entered. For example,

Do you eat bananas? _____ (Yes/No)

or

Do You eat bananas?   ☐ **Yes** ☐ **No**

There are, of course, times when the question and answer may occupy two or more lines. For instance,

How often do you use your SUPERIOR MEAT GRINDER?

☐ **Often**
☐ **Occasionally**
☐ **Seldom**
☐ **Not al all**

In such a case as this ensure that the question and answer options are clearly separated from any other question. This will avoid the possibility of a collection of answer options being associated with the wrong question.

14 If when constructing a question it is found to be very long yet impossible to shorten, try to divide it into sections. For example the following question,

If your Company car has an Original Market Value of less than £19,250 and is less than 4 years old give the size of the engine, if known, otherwise state it as unknown.

could be replace by

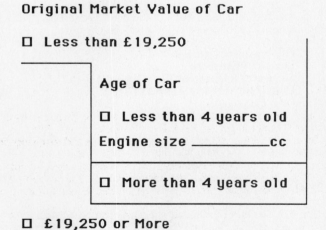

Original Market Value of Car

☐ **Less than £19,250**

> **Age of Car**
>
> ☐ **Less than 4 years old**
> **Engine size** _____cc
>
> ☐ **More than 4 years old**

☐ **£19,250 or More**

Notice how each section is blocked off clearly with boxes. This guides the eye and helps to clarify the question.

15 Do not make the questionnaire too long. Not only should the questions be short in length but they must also be few in number. Remember at all times that the questionnaire is an imposition despite the fact that some people do enjoy filling them in.

SEQUENCE OF QUESTIONS

16 Take care that the questions follow some form of natural sequence. For example, it would be misleading to ask how long a person had been married before asking if they were married

UNITS TO BE USED IN ANSWERS

17 If a question requires an answer in the form of a quantity then the units to be used must be clearly stated. It is also worth remembering that in England the population is divided into those who measure length in feet and inches and those who measure it in metres and centimetres. The same applies to weights. So clearly state the units and if possible allow for alternatives. For example

_____ **inches**

or

_____ **centimeters**

18 The units should also be stated in full and not abbreviated. For example

_____ **grammes**

rather than

_____ **gms**

DISTRIBUTION AND COLLECTION

19 Questionnaires can be delivered through the post or they can be delivered by those involved in the enquiry. The advantage of using the post is that it is cheaper. Personal delivery is more expensive but it does allow an opportunity for a representative to explain matters and to answer any queries.

20 The same applies to collection. If the questionnaire is to be returned by post then it should also include a post-paid, addressed envelope for the convenience of the respoondant. Again, personal collection does permit any problems of completing to be cleared up but it is an expensive option.

SUMMARY

21 The questionnaire is a very common method of obtaining data for s Statistical enquiry. When constructing a questionnaire the following four sections must be clearly defined;

Object and Authority
Stating why the information is being collected and who is asking for it

Instructions
Regarding when to complete and how to return the completed questionnaire

Details of the respondant
Assuring condfidentiality

Body of the enquiry
The questionnaire should consist of concise, unambiguous questions that are few in number.

At all times the respondant must be borne in mind recognising that the success of the questionnaire depends upon the repondant's goodwill.

KEY POINTS TO NOTE

22 Purpose, Object and Authority, Instructions, Details of Respondant, Body of the enquiry, Distribution

STUDENT SELF TESTING

SELF REVIEW QUESTIONS

1. What is the purpose of a questionnaire? (2)

2. List the 4 sections of a questionnaire. (3)

3. What are the Object and Authority of a questionnaire? (4)

4. List 3 instructions to be included in a questionnaire. (6)

5. How should we deal with long questions? (13,14)

6. How do we cater for units to be used in answers? (17)

7. List 2 methods of distributing questionnaires. (19,20)

EXERCISE (Answers begin on Page 249)

A large store employs 100 people. The management is attempting to discover how long it takes staff to travel to work each morning, and what (if any) delays they suffer.

Assume that all staff travel by one of the following methods;

a) by car, either driving themselves, or having a lift with someone else,

b) by bus, direct or needing a change of buses during the journey,

c) by train, by one of four local train services.

In b) and c) people may first have to walk to their local bus stop or station.

Design a questionnaire for staff to fill in themselves showing all this information. You may assume that the management knows where they live from personal records and that people can be identified by a reference number so that full name and address need not go on the questionnaire.

RSA 1985

6 When To Ask Questions

INTRODUCTION

1 The timing of questions has two problems associated with it. In this Chapter these two problems are addressed. Firstly, to ask questions there must be respondants who are both available and suitable. We consider alternative strategies when these conditions are not met. Secondly, questioners must be aware of the possibility of irrational answers. This can occur when the questions relate to highly topical and sensitive issues of the day.

This Chapter has two major sections. They are;

> **Availability Of Respondant**
> **Current Events**

AVAILABILITY OF RESPONDANT

2 The availability of the respondant can be separated into four distinct situations;

> **Temporarily Absent**
> **Absent For A Period**
> **Unsuitability Of Respondant**
> **Un-cooperative Respondant**

TEMPORARILY ABSENT

3 The problem of the respondant being absent temporarily can occur when the questionnaire is to be personally delivered or collected. This difficulty can be lessened by the timing of the call. The evening is generally the best time since many people are out at work during the day. If personal collection is desired and the respondants are out, leave a card stating who you are, why you called, when you called and when you will call again. Take care to chose a time different to the one that you have just tried.

ABSENT FOR A PERIOD

4 If the enquiry is for the puposes of finding out personal preferences for holidays then such an enquiry is best not held during the summer months. The very people you wish to ask may be away on holiday. If, after attempting a personal delivery there is still no sign of the occupants then a postal delivery could be substituted.

UNSUITABILITY OF THE RESPONDANT

5 Sometimes a respondant can be found to be unsuitable. There are, for example, members of certain ethnic communities who cannot speak English. Such people can be catered for by producing an alternative version in another language. In certain parts of the country, for example, the electoral register questionnaires are written in English, Guahati and Punjabi. Another alternative is to arrange for another person who speaks both English and the foreign language to act as an intermediary and fill in the form by proxy. The same principle can apply to blind respondents - they too will require assistance.

UN-COOPERATIVE REPONDANTS

6 Some respondants may plainly refuse to fill in the answers. There is little one can do to cater for these people other than accept their existence. It is reckoned that in any enquiry about 5 in every 100 will refuse to co-operate.

CURRENT EVENTS

7 Current events can affect the replies of the respondants and this fact must be recognised. It is quite noticeable, for example, that political party preferences swing dramatically during the Political Party Conference period in late summer. Immediately after a Political Party has had a Convention complete with all the TV coverage their popularity tends to increase. It would appear that there is nothing like a prevailing issue to focus the mind on a question. Immediately after the Three-Mile Island and Chernobyl nuclear power station disasters the general public were very concerned about the issues involved in nuclear power. Any enquiry on the nuclear issue that was conducted at that time would produce conclusions that would be biased by virtue of the recent catastrophic events.

When canvassing opinion one must try to ensure that the responses are rational and not over-influenced by emotion. Otherwise any conclusions will undoubtedly be biased and of questionable value as a basis for forming conclusions.

SUMMARY

8 Respondants may not be available to complete a questionnaire. If they are merely temporarily away then a second call at a different time could find them available. If they are away for an extended period then a postal delivery accompanied by instructions for returning the completed questionnaire could be substituted for a personal delivery. Respondants may not be suitable for filling in a questionnaire. In such cases the use of an intermediary to fill in the form may solve the problem. Some respondants may be simply un-cooperative but little can be done about them. Current events can cause repondants to answer irrationally. Such irrational anwswers are biassed and of little use.

KEY POINT TO NOTE

9 Availablity of respondants, Current events

STUDENT SELF TESTING

SELF REVIEW QUESTIONS

1. Give four reasons why a respondant may not be available. (2-6)

2. What effects do current events have on the respondant's answers? (7)

EXERCISE (Answers begin on Page 249)

In each of the following cases how would you expect the respondants replies to be affected by the timing of the questionnaire?

1 A questionnaire was distributed asking for opinions on laws affecting Trades Union. It was distributed at a time when a particular Union was engaged in a prolonged national strike that affected a large number of people.

2 A questionnaire was distributed asking for opinions of the Government's care of the poor and homeless. It was distributed during a spell of extremely cold weather with most of the country under a layer of snow.

Section 3   Collection Of Data

The second stage of a statistical enquiry concerns the collection of data. In this Section we look at the processes involved in gathering Primary Data. Having gathered data it has to be stored in a reference table for analysis. We consider the construction of these tables. Secondary data is considered as an alternatrive source of information. It is shown how to handle secondary data that is presented in tabular form. Certain features of data can be best revealed in graphical form and in the last chapter of this Section we discuss the elements of graph construction.

There are six Chapters in this Section. They are;

                        Chapter 1 : Primary Data
                        Chapter 2 : Probability And Sampling
                        Chapter 3 : Organising The Data
                        Chapter 4 : Tabulation of Data
                        Chapter 5 : Secondary Data
                        Chapter 6 : Graphical Representation Of Data

1 Primary Data

INTRODUCTION

1 This Chapter considers Primary Data. Primary Data is defined and various Government publications containing Primary Data are briefly reviewed. The means whereby Primary Data is collected is discussed at length.

There are four major parts to this Chapter. They are;

> **Primary Data**
> **Gathering Primary Data**
> **Surveys**
> **Non-Response**

PRIMARY DATA

2 Primary data is data that is collected first hand. The data is collected for a specific purpose and the collector is fully aware of both how it has been gathered and the subsequent processing it has undergone. As a result the accuracy and the relevance of Primary Data is fully understood by those responsible for collecting it. Unfortunately, since it requires a substantial labour force to collect it, Primary Data is very expensive to acquire. Because of this, the only organisations capable of collecting Primary Data are those with access to large amounts of money such as the Government and large Companies.

The Government gathers Primary Data to enable it to govern effectively. They need to be able to measure the results of their actions and to plan future policies. For this they require, and they obtain, vast amount of data which is susequently published in various Journals. Typical of these Journals are the

> **Monthly Digest of Statistics**
> **Financial Statistics**
> **Employment Gazette**

MONTHLY DIGEST OF STATISTICS

3 The Digest is published each month by Her Majesty's Stationery Office. Its contents are prepared by the Central Statistical Office (a section of the Civil Service) and the Statistical Divisions of various Government Departments. The purpose of the Digest is to provide a continual statistical description of the state of the country. To this end it covers a very wide spectrum of topics. These topics range from those of a general nature such as the National Income Expenditure and External Trade through those concerned with Industry such as Industrial Production and Agriculture to those concerned with the populace such as Social Services. The Annual Abstract of Statistics contains much of the contents of the Digest in even greater detail.

FINANCIAL STATISTICS

4 Financial Statistics is prepared each month by the Central Statistical Office, the Statistical Divisions of Government Departments and the Bank of England. It is a very important publication dealing with the financial statistics of the United Kingdom. The contents include details of the Government's revenue and spending, local authority borrowing, banking statistics and the financial statistics of various large companies.

EMPLOYMENT GAZETTE

5 This monthly publication is prepared by the Department of Trade and deals with all aspects of manpower and employment. Amongst its many topics it details wages, hours worked and retail prices.

6 Government data abounds and a visit to your local Public Library is highly recommended. It is only by viewing these and other publications at first hand that a true feel for the scope of this aspect of Primary Data can be obtained.

7 Many Companies will gather Primary Data within their own organisation to assist them in their administration and planning. A few large Companies will have the financial wherewithal to obtain Primary Data on specific markets from outside their organisation. Before a new product can be launched an expensive marketing enquiry will be undertaken. The Company must be able to identify and to quantify a market for the product. Only if the market is large enough and the future projected profits sufficient will the Company launch the product. To enable this will require an expensive Market Survey. We look at Market Surveys later in this Chapter.

GATHERING PRIMARY DATA

8 There are a number of methods of gathering Primary Data. We shall look at

> **Interviews**
> **Questionnaires**
> **Diaries**

INTERVIEWS

9 The interview method of collecting data allows a respondant to be asked questions on a person to person basis. There are two methods of executing the interview, they are;

> **Direct Interview**
> **Indirect Interview**

DIRECT INTERVIEW

10 In the direct interview the questionner and the respondant face each other. The success of the interview will depend upon the skill and personality of the interviewer.

SKILL

11 Amongst the various skills the interviewer must posses are the ability to manage people, the ability to listen and the abiltiy to put the respondant at ease. The interviewer must be able to pesuade the respondant to answer the questions. To some people these skills come naturally, others have to acquire them through formal training courses.

PERSONALITY

12 The interviewer must be lively and give the impression of interest in the answers to the questions even if the respondant is the hundredth person they have interviewed that day. The interviewer must possess;

Tact
Neutrality
Amiability
Accuracy

TACT

13 The interviewer must neither offend nor generate hostility in the person being interviewed. Otherwise the answers will reflect that immediate hostility rather than the considered opinion.

NEUTRALITY

14 The interviewer's feeling about the questions must not be allowed to colour the respondants feelings thereby affecting the answers.

AMIABILITY

15 Keep it cheerful. If there is no fun there will be little point and it will be difficult to maintain the interest of the person being interviewed.

ACCURACY

16 The phrasing of questions must be accurate and the answers must be accurately acquired and accurately recorded.

INDIRECT INTERVIEW

17 The indirect interview could be by telephone where the interviewer and the person being interviewed are remote from one another. In this situation the interviewer must establish his or her skills without the benefit of eye contact. Because of this additional skills are required. These concern;

Manner
Clarity
Brevity

MANNER

18 The interviewers manner must be pleasing and cheerful even in the face of hostility. At all times the interviewer must be polite.

CLARITY

19 The interviewer should ensure that he or she speaks clearly and distincly. The questions should be particularly short.

BEVITY

20 Keep the entire interview as short as possible otherwise the respondant may lose interest.

QUESTIONNAIRE

21 The use of a questionnaire as a means of gathering primary data has been considered in the last Chapter. As we saw there are two basic types of Questionnaire, the postal and the non-postal. The advantage of a postal questionnaire is that it can be cheaply distributed to a large number of people. The disadvantages are that there is usually a poor level of response and it is not easy to explain any questions in the event of a query. On the other hand, a non-postal Questionnaire, delivered door-to-door may have a higher response rate but the cost of distribution is far higher. For this reason the distribution would be limited to fewer people.

THE POPULATION CENSUS

22 The Population Census is a Government questionnaire distributed to all householders every ten years. Though the idea of a Census is very old - the Babylonians were taking them 4,000 years ago - the first British Census was not held until 1801. The purpose of the Census is to provide information on social, economic and population conditions to allow the Government to plan future policy. It is completed by every householder in the country on one specified evening. Because of the widespread distribution the handling of the Census is very expensive and time consuming. It requires an elaborate organisation to distribute it with upwards of 100,000 enumeration districts and a number of years to analyse it. To ensure a complete enumeration it is compulsory to fill it in. To enable this the questionnaire is preceded by a Census Act that makes it a criminal offence not to comply with the requirements.

The questionnaire is in three parts dealing with;

> **Housing**
> **People present on Census night**
> **People usually present but absent on Census night.**

By taking such a 'snapshot' view of the country's population it is possible to measure population movement both within the country and without and to predict the size of the population in the future with a reasonable degree of accuracy.

DIARY

23 A diary is a record of all the events that happen to a group of people in relation to some specific facet of life. For example, The Family Expenditure Survey and the Viewing Diary in the USA. In the Family Expenditure Survey a number of families each keep a diary of their expediture over a given period. In the Viewing Diary a selection of household record their television viewing. This is of assistance to the various television Companies when planning their future programmes. In the USA a large number of the television programmes are sponsored by specific advertisers. In order to convince the advertisers that there will be sufficient viewers to see their commercials the television companies use the results of the Viewing Diaries.

ADVANTAGES OF A DIARY

24 A complete record of a group of families can be obtained thereby allowing very accurate data to be obtained.

DISADVANTAGES OF A DIARY

25 Only the more educated and aware people are likely to keep the diary fully maintained. Since the diary is supposed to record all events pertinent to an enquiry it will inevitably be biased towards these more aware individuals.

SURVEYS

26 Surveys are fact finding exercises that are carried out by various means such as interviews, questionnaires or diaries. The particular types of survey of interest here are;

> **Pilot Survey**
> **Panel Survey**
> **Longtitudinal Survey**
> **Market Research Survey**
> **Public Opinion Polls**

PILOT SURVEY

27 A pilot survey is a small scale replica of an eventual full scale survey. It provides basic information such as the effectiveness of the questions on a questionnaire. It is a small investigative survey that esatablishes the procedures and the analysis prior to the issuing of the questionnaire in the full blown survey.

PANEL SURVEY

28 In a panel survey a particular group - called a panel - is asked a series of questions on different occasions so that the changing reactions and awareness of individuals can be monitored. They can be used to test the effectiveness of an advertising campaign by asking questions before and after the compaign. In this way their reactions can be accurately measured.

LONGTITUDINAL SURVEY

29 This is the same as a panel survey but the monitoring of the group continues over an extended period of time. For example, a selection of children can be continually inspected to monitor their growth patterns over the entire period of their childhood. In this way conclusions can be obtained regarding child growth patterns within the entire population.

MARKET RESEARCH SURVEY

30 A Company will use the Market Research survey to discover who uses their product and why they use it in preference to a competing product. Market Research Surveys monitor buying habits. Test reaction to packaging. Collect opinions. They are usually executed by paid interviewers and some companies exist purely to perform Market Research for other companies. It is an expensive operation.

PUBLIC OPINION POLLS

31 A Public Opinion Poll is a survey that obtains the opinions of members of the public on one or more issues. A more detailed discussion of Public Opinion Polls is given in the next Chapter.

NON-RESPONSE

32 Non-response must always be borne in mind when considering the results of a survey. There is really very little that one can be done to remedy non-response but awareness of non-response is necessary because it is a source of error. It is possible for a badly handled survey to generate a non-response amongst the very people that it was aimed at. In every human situation the person observed is affected by the person observing - even observing by asking questions. For example, a Systems Analyst studying the working habits of a Company's labour force may find a level of resentment against his presence. This resentment could then affect the Analyst's observations to such an extent that his ultimate conclusions may be at best suspect and at worst invalid.

SUMMARY

33 Primary Data is data gathered at first hand and is very expensive to acquire. The Government gathers a vast amount of Primary Data to enable it to govern and this data appears in a number of publications. We have considered three ways of gathering Primary Data. The interview is a person-to-person confrontation and requires distinct interviewing skills. The questionnaire is a more remote method of collecting Primary Data and suffers from a poor response rate. The diary is a method of continually gathering data from a fixed number of people and can be a very valuable source of information.

Within the wider area of Statistical Enquiries we have considered various types of Survey, namely;

> **Pilot survey**
> **Panel survey**
> **Longtitudinal survey**
> **Market research survey**
> **Public opinion polls**

KEY POINTS TO NOTE

34 Primary data, Sources of primary data, Interviews, Population census, Diary, Surveys, Public Opinion Polls, Non-response

STUDENT SELF TESTING

SELF REVIEW QUESTIONS

1. What is Primary Data? (2)

2. List 3 sources of primary data. (3-6)

3. Why do some Companies collect primary data? (7)

4. List the requirements for an interviewer conducting a direct interview, (10-16), an indirect interview. (17-20)

5. List the advantages and disadvantages of postal and non-postal questionnaires. (21)

6. What is the Population Census? (22)

7. What is a Diary? (23)

8. What are the advantages and disadvantages of a Diary? (24,25)

8. List 5 types of survey. (27-31)

EXERCISES (Answers begin on Page 249)

1 Briefly describe the contents of two sources of Primary Data published by Her Majesty's Stationery Office on behalf of the Government.

2 Distinguish between the skills required for a direct interview and an indirect interview.

3 What is the Population Census and what uses are made of the data obtained from the Census?

4 Discuss the use of a Diary as a source of Primary Data.

5 Write notes on the following

        a) Pilot Surveys
        b) Panel Surveys
        c) Longtitudinal Surveys

2 Probability And Sampling

INTRODUCTION

1 This Chapter opens with a discussion of the need for and the problems of taking samples from a population. It continues with a very elementary introduction to probability and its use in selecting random samples. Various different types of sample are considered and the Chapter concludes with a discussion on Public Opinion Polls.

There are five major parts to this Chapter. They are;

> **The Need To Sample**
> **Elements Of Probability**
> **Sampling From a Population**
> **Types Of Sample**
> **Public Opinion Polls**

THE NEED TO SAMPLE

2 A Sample is a group of people taken from an entire population. For example, the people that live in your street are a sample of the entire pouplation of the town in which you live. If a survey was to be conducted in your town then it would be out of the question for the interviewers to approach every single person living in the town. It would be far too costly and take far too long. Instead, the interviewers would approach a sample of the town's population thereby ensuring quicker and cheaper results.

3 The problem that arises in selecting a sample concerns who to select to form the sample. The sample should be so chosen that it is a small scale replica of the entire population. In this way it is said to REPRESENT or BE REPRESENTATIVE of the population. To explain this further let us assume that in your town 30 people out of every 100 are employed, 10 people out of every 100 are registered as un-employed and 25 people out of every 100 are schoolchildren. Any sample that represents this population should have the same proportions. That is, if the sample consisted of just 100 people, 30 of them should be employed, 10 of them should be registered as unemployed and 25 of them should be schoolchildren. From the results obtained from the sample we can then infer results applicable to the entire population. All this because the sample represents the population.

4 A sample could be collected, as mentioned earlier, by taking everybody who lived in your street. Unfortunately this easy solution is not really a good solution. There are more different types of people living in your town than there are people living in your street. So your street cannot possibly represent the entire town. By chosing the people in your street you are PURPOSELY leaving out those people who cannot be represented. When a representative sample is selected then its members must be chosen in such a manner that no one type of individual is PURPOSELY LEFT OUT. If you purposefully left out all left-handed writers then the sample would be biased against such people - it could in no way represent them. To achieve an unbiased sample we must select people from the population in such a manner that every member of the population has an equal chance of being selected. To do this we need to know a little bit about CHANCE or, as it is also known, PROBABILITY.

ELEMENTS OF PROBABILITY

5 If a coin is tossed into the air it is probable that it will come down heads. It is equally probable that it will come down tails. We can measure this PROBABLE-NESS. There are two possibilities for the eventual outcome of the coin - it comes down heads or it comes down tails. We say that it has 1 chance in 2 of coming down heads - there is 1 head and 2 possibilites. The PROBABLE-NESS of a head we call the PROBABILITY of a head and measure it as

$$1 \div 2 = 0.5$$

Similarly the probabiltiy of a tail is also 0.5. Take a further example. Select a card from a deck of 52 playing cards. How many chances are there that it is a SPADE? There are 13 SPADES in the pack so there are 13 chances in 52 of it being a SPADE. We say that the PROBABILITY of drawing a SPADE from a deck of 52 cards is

$$13 \div 52 = 0.25$$

CERTAINTY AND IMPOSSIBILITY

6 If an event is CERTAIN to happen we say that it has a PROBABILITY of 1. For example, if we toss a double-headed coin what is the chance of it coming up haeds. There are 2 heads and 2 possible landings so the probabilty is

$$2 \div 2 = 1.$$

What is the PROBABILITY of it coming up tails? there are 0 tails and 2 possible landings so the PROBABILITY of a tail is

$$0 \div 2 = 0.$$

It is an IMPOSSIBLE outcome - there is no tail on a double-headed coin. We say that if an outcome is IMPOSSIBLE then it has a PROBABILITY of 0. The probabilities of POSSIBLE but NOT CERTAIN outcomes are all numbers greater than 0 and less than 1.

PRESETTING PROBABILITIES

7 How are we to assign probabilities to outcomes. In the case of drawing cards from a deck of 52 cards we can assume that any card is equally likely to be chosen so that any card has a probabiltiy of

1/52 of being chosen. In practice we know that this is not true. Those cards near the edge of a fan of cards are less likely to be chosen and those nearest the centre are more likely to be chosen. The net effect of this is that presetting the probabilities in this way is not very satisfactory. What we can do instead is to rely on STATISTICAL REGULARITY.

STATISTICAL REGULARITY

8 If a coin is tossed 1000 times during which time it comes up heads 510 times and tails 490 times then we could conclude that the coin is slightly biased towards heads - the probability of a head is

$$510 \div 1000 = 0.51$$

and the probability of a tail is

$$490 \div 1000 = 0.49.$$

This is the principle of statistical regularity. By constantly repeating an experiment and counting the occurence of its outcomes we can arrive at the probability of any particular outcome occurring. This method of assigning probabilities is subject to error, of course. If the same coin had been tossed 2000 times we might have found that the coin came up heads 980 times and tails 1020 times. In this case the probability of a head would then be calculated as

$$980 \div 2000 = 0.49$$

and of tails

$$1020 \div 2000 = 0.51$$

exactly the opposite conclusion to the previous one. The point is that one has to stop repeating the experiment sometime and base one's conclusions on the results so found - therein lies the error.

SAMPLING FROM A POPULATION

9 When planning a survey one is attempting to find out information about a particular group of people. This group of people is called the POPULATION - sometimes referred to as the TARGET POPULATION. For example, if you are a manufacturer of a teenage lipstick then the target population would be all females between the ages of 13 and 19 inclusive. If you were a manufacturer of dog food and were planning a survey to measure the reaction to a newly introduced type of dog food then the target population of your survey would be all dog owners.

10 Once the target population has been clearly identified it will in all likelihood consist of a very large number of people located in widely scattered locations. To approach everyone in the target population with your list of questions would be impossible - it would take far too long and would be far too expensive. What is done is to select a SAMPLE of people from that population that is representative of that population. The sample must, in effect, be a small scale replica of the target population. For example if 10 in every 100 of the entire target population thoroughly detested your product this fact must be reflected in your sample - 10 in evey 100 of the sample must also thoroughly detest your product. In this way, by measuring properties of the sample we can INFER properties of the target population. We must be able to say, for example, that if 32 in every 100 of the sample like the colour blue for their underwear then we can infer that 32 in every 100 of the target population will like the color blue for their underwear. The next problem to consider is that of actually selecting these representative samples.

SELECTING SAMPLES

11 Selecting samples is very easy but selecting samples that are representative of a population is very difficult. If we are to select a sample from the population of a town then we can select names from the telephone directory or from the local registry of electors. The location from which we select our sample is called the SAMPLING FRAME - in this last case the Electoral Register is the sampling frame. If we are to select a sample from the population of the local school we could select names from the enrollment register. We could even stand at the gates and select students as they left school. Selecting samples is easy but so often our method of selection introduces errors.

ERRORS

12 Sampling is subject to two types of error;

Bias
Sampling error

BIAS

13 If we select names from a telephone directory then we are introducing a BIAS. All the people that we select will have telephones. Those people who do not have a phone cannot be selected. This produces a biased sample - it is biased towards those people who possess a telephone (or conversly, it is also biased against those people who do not have a telephone). Consequently, any results obtained from a study of that sample will only apply to people who have telephones. If we select a sample by standing outside the gate of a school then we miss those pupils who were absent. The absentees have no possiblility whatsoever of being in the sample. This again is a biased sample. If we select a sample by interviewing people in the street as so many surveys do then the only people who can be selected are from amongst those people that are there. The sample is biased towards those people who happened to be in that street at that particular time.

SAMPLING ERROR

14 The second source of error is the SAMPLING ERROR. This can be measured. It is the difference between the value of a statistic obtained from the sample and the value of the same statistic obtained from the entire population. However, we have already said that measuring the entire population is not feasible so in reality it is not possible to actually measure the sampling error. What we can do, however, is to increase the size of the sample - this reduces the error.

THE LAW OF LARGE NUMBERS

15 The Law of Large Numbers states that as the sample size increases the sampling error decreases. In the limit where the sample has increased to include the entire population then obviously there is no sampling error at all - the difference is zero. Clearly it is virtually impossible to totally eliminate sampling error. However, we can at least reduce the sampling error by eliminating bias in our choice of members of the sample.

RANDOM SAMPLES

16 The only sample that is free of bias is the RANDOM SAMPLE. If a sample is chosen from a target population under the proviso that every member of the population has an equal chance of being selected for the sample then that sample is called a RANDOM SAMPLE. The word RANDOM does not mean haphazzard - on the contrary selecting a random sample is a very systematic process. The word RANDOM means that each member of the population has the same PROBABILITY of being selected for the sample.

17 Let us consider a survey that has as its target population the population of an entire town that is over the age of 18. Going to the Public Library will allow us to consult the register of electors. Every person who has a vote - that is every person over the age of 18 - will have a number at the side of their name. This number is their Electoral Register Number. Let us assume that there are 100,000 people on the register and that we wish to select a sample of size 100. We must, therefore, select 1 out of every 1000 of the electors on the electoral roll under the proviso that every person on the list has the same probabiltiy of being selected

$$1/100,000 = 0.00001.$$

How do we do it?

18 We could you might think select every 1000th name going down the list but this means that we have decided beforehand who is to be selected **once the first name has been chosen**. This is not a random selection. Having selected the first name the next name should come from **anywhere** on the list if the selection is to be random and not from the 1000th name further down the list. To achieve a random sample we must first of all produce a list of 100 numbers lying between 1 and 100,000 that are chosen at random. We can do this by writing a simple little computer program or alternatively by using a table of random numbers. Once we have obtained our random list of 100 numbers lying between 1 and 100,000 we then select from the electoral register those names that appear opposite those numbers. In this way we select a random sample. It should be noted that the random sample chosen is not necessarily the BEST sample that could have been chosen - we only know that it is a sample that is free of bias. The BEST sample would not only be free of bias but would also be free of sampling error. We do not know whether our sample is representative of the population or not but at least it is not **intentionally non-representative**, that is it is not biased.

FURTHER BIAS ERRORS

19 Even after selecting our random sample that is free of bias we can still subject the survey to bias errors. This could be done, for example, by a failure to cover the entire sample or by using non-randomly chosen substitutes in place of non-responses. This explains why it is so important to be aware of non-response. If a random sample has been selected for a questionnaire then the complete sample must covered if we are to conclude that our findings are representative of the complete population. As soon as substitutes are obtained for those people who do not respond then a bias can be introduced by the very act of selecting them. If non-responses are ignored then a bias is introduced by the very act of ignoring them.

TYPES OF SAMPLE

20 Even within the category of random samples there are different types of sample that are used for specific purposes. Those that we shall briefly consider are as follows;

>   **Quota Samples**
>   **Multi-Stage Samples**
>   **Cluster samples**
>   **Systematic Samples**
>   **Stratified Samples**

QUOTA SAMPLES

21 In a quota sample the proportions of people to be chosen are pre-set. For example, if a male to female quota is pre-set at 2 males for every 3 females then a sample of 100 must be chosen so that it contains 40 males and 60 females. The quota is chosen so that they are representative of the population in **one or two respects** but not necessarily in others. The other respects are assumed unimportant for the particular survey. For instance a quota sample may consist of men, women and children in the same proportions as the target population but with an ethnic mix that was not representative of the target population.

MULTI-STAGE SAMPLES

22 A multi-stage sample is a random sample of a random sample. For example, if we were to sample the population living in 100 streets then we could first of all randomly select say 10 streets from the 100. Having done this we would then randomly select people from the 10 chosen streets - this is a random sample of people from a random sample of streets.

CLUSTER SAMPLING

23 This is the same as multi-stage sampling with the final sampling done according to specific characteristics. For example, having chosen our ten streets we could then chose a sample of blue eyed brunettes from the 10 streets - the blue eyed brunette being the specific characteristics.

SYSTEMATIC SAMPLES

24 Systematic samples are of the type previously mentioned where names are selected from a list by chosing a name at regular intervals such as every 100th name. These samples are biased against those people who have no chance of being chosen once the first name has been selected.

STRATIFIED SAMPLES

25 In a stratified sample the population is divided into blocks where all the members of a block have at least one feature in common. For example, the population could be divided into three blocks, namely those under 21 years old, those who are aged between 21 and 40 and finally those over 40 years old. In this way no one person is in more than one block. The random samples are then chosen from each block.

PUBLIC OPINION POLLS

26 A Public Opinion Poll is a survey designed to gather information on opinions and intentions. The public referred to consists of those individuals who are in the position to have valid opinions about the subject matter of the poll. For example, in a poll designed to obtain opinions about the popularity of the Government the public chosen would be the nation's electorate. In a poll about home-ownership a public consisting of just home-owners may be more appropriate.

A number of companies execute public opinion polls and their results are regularly published in various newspapers. For example, the GALLUP POLL is published in the Daily Telegraph, NATIONAL OPINION POLLS publish in the Daily Mail, MARPLAN publish in the Times and OPINION RESEARCH CENTRE publishes in the Sunday Times.

27 The polls are executed on samples chosen from the public. These samples are usually random samples or quota samples. Random sampling is preferred since the level of sampling error can be calculated and the probability of obtaining a representative sample is high. It is possible to show, for instance, that 95 times out of a 100 we can be certain that the results produced from a random sample of 2,000 electors will be reasonably accurate. This assumes, of course, that the respondant's replies are honest and unbiased.

28 In a stratified random sample for a political poll the country is divided into 10 regions. Within each region the electoral constituencies are divided into urban, rural and political party of the sitting Member of Parliament. The effect of this is to produce a list of all the country's constituencies that are stratified according to specific attributes. From this list 200 constituencies are selected at random. From within each constituency so selected 20 specific electors are randomly chosen to produce a complete sample of 4,000 electors. This method of polling can be very accurate but it is very expensive to execute. Every single person selected for the sample must to be interviewed and this can mean multiple visits by the interviewer. Also each new poll has to reselect a completely new sample.

29 To overcome the problems of non-response and the costs of administering random samples many polls use quota samples. The constituencies are selected in the same manner as for stratified sampling but the individual interviewees are selected according to pre-set quotas. The quotas are derived from the population proportions given in the Census returns and other such publications. The quotas will then dictate, for example, how many men and how many women are to be chosen by the interviewer. The pollsters then interview in the street according to these pre-set quotas. This has the advantage of eliminating non-response - if one person refuses to answer then another is approached. Also, since the same quotas are used for all samples, the cost of administration is substantially reduced. Unfortunately, the final sample may not be representative of the population. For example, the elderly and infirm tend to be left out.

30 Predicting future intentions of the public from the results of the polls is very problematical. The voting public can have changing opinions between elections. If the election is too far off then opinions may only reflect the popularity of the Government and not really indicate a future voting intention.

SUMMARY

31 It is both very costly and very time consuming to survey very large populations. To reduce cost and to speed up a statistical enquiry we survey a sample of the population. This sample must be representative of the population. To ensure that it is representative is a difficult problem. All non-representative samples posses sampling errors and bias. Sampling error can be reduced by increasing the size of the sample. Bias can be eliminated by selecting a Random Sample. A Random Sample is a sample where every member of the population has an equal chance of being selected for the sample. Various types of sample have been reviewed, namely;

> **Quota Samples**
> **Multi-Stage Samples**
> **Cluster samples**
> **Systematic Samples**
> **Stratified Samples**

Finally we considered Public Opinion Polls.

KEY POINTS TO NOTE

32 Samples, Presetting probabilities, Statistical regularity, Target population, Sampling errors, Law of large numbers, Random samples, Bias errors, Types of sample, Public opinion polls

STUDENT SELF TESTING

1. Why do we sample? (2)

2. How should the sample relate to the population? (3,4,9,10)

3. What is Probability and how can it be used to distinguish between Certainty and Impossibility. (5,6)

4. How are probabilities preset? (7)

5. What is statistical regularity? (8)

6. What are bias errors and how can they be reduced? (13,19)

7. What is a random sample? (16-18)

8. What are sample errors and how can they be reduced? (14,15)

9. List 5 types of sample. (20-25)

10 How representative of public opinion are Public Opinion Polls? (26-30)

EXERCISES (Answers begin on Page 249)

1 What role does probability play in the selection of a sample from a target population?

2 A shop-floor committee of 8 is to be selected from four departments in a manufacturing company. There are a total of 400 individuals to choose from. The four departments contain 80, 120, 100 and

100 people respectively. Describe briefly how you would select such a committee by

> a) Random sampling
> b) Stratified sampling
> c) Quota sampling

3 What are sampling errors and how do they differ from bias errors?

4 Below are 5 choices of sampling method;

> Random sampling
> Stratified sampling
> Quota sampling
> Cluster sampling

Which sampling method would you think was used in each of the following situations;

a) A Headmaster used random number tables to select 50 pupils to interview about homework.

b) In a health survey a local clinic questioned all patients over the age of 40.

c) In a survey to determine musical tastes, 100 people under the age of 18 and 60 people over the age of 65 were interviewed.

5 The following table records where individuals spend their leisure time. The individuals were selected by a market research team.

a) What can you conclude from the Sports Centre column?

b) What does the TV column suggest?

c) Why do you think that the 'other' column is empty for Women?

d) How representative of the general population do you think these results are?

	TV	Cinema	Theatre	Sport	Other
Men	85	15	5	9	3
Women	89	3	4	6	–
Age 20-30	76	12	12	25	4
Age 65+	92	–	5	–	10

3 Organising The Data

INTRODUCTION

1 This Chapter deals with the organisation of data. Having gathered the data in the form of completed questionnaires or data sheets the data must be organised before it can be analysed. This organisation consists of editing the data and then sorting it. Sorting could also include ranking and counting the data.

There are four major parts to this Chapter. They are;

> **Editing The Data**
> **Sorting The Questionnaires**
> **Ranking The Data**
> **Counting The Data**

EDITING THE DATA

2 Once the questionnaire has been completed we must

> **Check for completeness**
> **Check for accuracy**
> **Enter calculated numbers**
> **Code answers**

CHECKING FOR COMPLETENESS

3 The questions on the questionnaire must be checked to ensure that they have all been answered. Any questionnaires that have not been completed must then be set aside for consideration later. It may be that some of the answers can be included in the final results.

CHECKING FOR ACCURACY

4 The answers must be checked where possible for accuracy. Check that the address contains the post code, for example. Check that answers are in the correct place on the questionnaire. If possible, amend any innaccuracies.

ENTERING CALCULATED NUMBERS

5 As mentioned earlier, respondants should not be required to make any calculations. However, calculations may be necessary to complete the information required. It is at this editing stage that those answers requiring numerical calculation are inserted.

CODING ANSWERS

6 Multi-choce answers are best numerically coded for later analysis. This code can be entered during editing

7 After editing there may still be questionnaires that contain incomplete, or inaccurate data. These questionnaires should be set to one side and considered as a separate group. It may be that some of the data they contain can be used. A record should also be kept of all those questionnaires that were not filled in. In this way some measure of the non-response can be made.

SORTING THE QUESTIONNAIRES

8 Once the data has been edited it may be desireable to sort the questionnaires prior to analysing the data that they contain. For example, it may be desired to have male and female respondents identified separately. Or it may be desired to identify data corresponding to particular income groups. In either case the questionnaires can be sorted into their appropriate groups. The advantage of this sorting is that it will make it easier to extract data for analysis at a later time.

RANKING THE DATA

9 Once the questionnaires have been sorted into groups they may be further sorted into subgroups. They could be sorted according to one particular datum on the questionnaire. For example, suppose a sample of ten people had been asked for their weight. These weights could then be read off as follows

Weight in lbs

140 165 135 180 202 154 172 193 137 146

Having done this they can then be sorted into order of size as follows

Weight in lbs

135 137 140 146 154 165 172 180 193 202

This is called RANKING in ASCENDING ORDER. If our data were names then we could rank in alphabetical order starting with the A's and working through to the Z's.

Ranking of data in this way allows COUNTING OF FREQUENCIES to be easily achieved.

COUNTING THE DATA

10 Once ranked the data can now be counted. Suppose a stratified sample had been surveyed and that one of the questions had asked for the age of the respondant. Suppose further that there were 30 people in the strata block aged 40 - 45. We could then read off the ages of the respondants and list them as follows;

        40 42 41 43 44 45 45 45 44 40
        43 42 40 43 42 45 44 41 41 42
        44 40 41 45 44 43 44 41 42 45

These numbers could then be ranked in ascending order allowing us to COUNT their frequencies as follows;

                                                                    Frequency

        40 40 40 40   **4**
        41 41 41 41 41   **5**
        42 42 42 42   **5**
        43 43 43 43   **4**
        44 44 44 44 44 44   **6**
        45 45 45 45 45 45   **6**
                                TOTAL   **30**

The TOTAL is a check. The frequencies should all add up to the total number of ages listed.

By RANKING and COUNTING data in this way a preliminary analysis of the data has been achieved.

SUMMARY

11 Having gathered in all the data from the preliminary stages of a statistical enquiry the data must undergo a certain amount of organizing before it can be analysed. This organisation consists of editing and sorting. Editing checks for completeness and accuracy. It also allows calculated figures to be entered on the questionnaires and for multiple choice answers to be coded. Having edited the data the questionnaires can be sorted into groups and subgroups. This will make it easier to extract data for analysis at a later time. A preliminary analysis can be performed by ranking and counting specific data on each questionnaire.

KEY POINTS TO NOTE

12 Editing the data, Sorting questionnairs, Ranking data, Counting data

STUDENT SELF TESTING

SELF REVIEW QUESTIONS

1. List the processes involved in editing data. (2-7)

2. Why may it be desireable to sort questionnaires? (8)

3. What is the purpose of ranking data? (9,10)

EXERCISES (Answers begin on Page 249)

1 Describe the processes involved in editing data obtained via a questionnaire.

2 A small engineering firm has recorded the bonuses paid to its eleven workshop staff in the following table;

Bonuses (£)

13.76	14.73	12.98	9.96	22.43
11.69	12.74	17.68	16.93	17.54
14.64				

Rank this data in ascending order.   **RSA 1986**

3 A questionnaire was distributed to a sample drawn from a particular city. The questionnaire was set to find out how much people used public transport. Suggest categories into which the questionnaires could be sorted.

4 The number of defective transistors recorded in 50 successive production runs are recorded below;

```
4 8 6 5 3 2 1 9 4 1
3 5 2 8 7 2 2 3 5 1
7 5 7 4 1 5 6 8 4 5
6 1 3 1 6 4 2 1 8 7
2 4 6 4 3 1 2 9 3 4
```

Rank and count this data to obtain its frequencies.

4 Tabulation Of Data

INTRODUCTION

1 Once data has been gathered it has to be collated into a form that is useful for analysis. The form in which it is usually collated is the TABLE. In this Chapter we first consider DATA ATTRIBUTES and then discuss how measured values of the attributes can be TABULATED. Specific pointers for table construction are considered. Finally, different types of tables are described.

There are four major parts to this Chapter. They are;

> **Data Attributes**
> **Tables**
> **Table Construction**
> **Types of Reference Table**

DATA ATTRIBUTES

2 Data can refer to a variety of things. It can refer to age, to weight, to colour, to texture. These things we call the data ATTRIBUTES. Such attributes can be

> **Measureable Attributes**
> **Descriptive Attributes**

MEASUREABLE ATTRIBUTES

3 Many types of data can be quantified. Metres, days, tonnes for example are typical units of quantity. Any data that has an attribute that has such units associated with it is called a measureable attribute. Measureable attributes can be

> **Discrete Attributes**
> **Continuous Attributes**

DISCRETE ATTRIBUTES

4 Attributes that are measured by a collection of numbers with gaps between them are called DISCRETE attributes. For example, postage is a discrete attribute as it is measured in whole units of 1p.

CONTINUOUS ATTRIBUTES

5 Attributes that are measured by numbers with no gaps between them are called CONTINUOUS attributes. For example, height can be measured in metres to any desired degree of accuracy on a continuous scale of numbers.

DESCRIPTIVE ATTRIBUTES

6 The attributes that cannot be measured are called DESCRIPTIVE attributes. For example, colour, feeling, loudness.

TABLES

7 Tables are used for storing data in the form of quantity or description of attributes. The following tabel records the numbers of cars and vans in a car park that were either blue or green.

	VANS	CARS
BLUE	5	8
GREEN	0	2

The attribute NUMBER OF BLUE VANS is measureable - there were 5 of them.

There are two basic types of table

Reference Tables
Demonstration Tables

REFERENCE TABLES

8 Reference Tables are used to store data for further use. There are a number of types of reference table and these will be looked at later in this Chapter.

DEMONSTRATION TABLES

9 Demonstration Tables are used for displaying the results of a statistical enquiry. They are used to summarize data and not to store data for future use. This type of table will be looked at in detail in Chapter 3 of Section 5.

TABLE CONSTRUCTION

10 For every type of table there are a number of rules to be followed when constructing them. These rules concern;

> **Columnar Layout**
> **Spacing And Partitions**
> **Column And Row Labels**
> **Multiple Rows and Columns**
> **Arrangement Of Data**
> **Space For Calculated Data**
> **Headers And Footers**

COLUMNAR LAYOUT

11 The entries in a table have to be easily located and accurately read. For these reasons the entries are placed in well-defined ROWS and COLUMNS. This is called COLUMNAR LAYOUT. The following diagram illustrates this feature.

	COLUMN 1	COLUMN 2	COLUMN3
ROW 1	1.23	2.30	19
ROW 2	3.45	4.00	217
ROW 3	5.67	6.57	3142

Notice how the entries are placed. The decimal points are all under each other and the whole numbers in the third column are RIGHT JUSTIFIED - that is they all have the respective units, tens, hundreds and so on under each other.

SPACING AND PARTITIONS

12 As shown in the previous diagram the rows and columns are partitioned with vertical and horizontal lines. This produces a table whose entries are easily located. Also there is sufficient space in each CELL to hold the entry without appearing cramped. This allows the data to be easily read. Notice also that the numbers are separated from the words by double lines. The words are called the row and column LABELS and they are separated from the body of the table by this means.

COLUMN AND ROW LABELS

13 It must be clear what the entries in the table refer to. This is achieved by putting a description at the head of each row and column. The following table records the daily takings from two tills in a local greengrocery store.

	MON	TUE	WEDS	THUR	FRI	SAT
TILL 1	120.60	110.50	150.60	145.18	134.26	185.70
TILL 2	98.46	104.23	110.05	99.97	108.14	123.40

Notice how the columns have been labelled with abbreviations for the days of the week. This is permissable because these abbreviations are common knowledge. If abbreviations are used that are not commonly understood then a KEY must be given to explain them. We consider KEYS in paragraph **19** of this Chapter.

This table in this example is particularly straightforward. It becomes a little more awkward when there are MULTIPLE ROWS or COLUMNS

MULTIPLE ROWS AND COLUMNS

14 Some tables have a group of columns or rows under a single label. The following table records the number of students, male and female, in three classrooms on two successive days.

	ROOM 1		ROOM 2		ROOM 3	
	MALE	FEMALE	MALE	FEMALE	MALE	FEMALE
THURSDAY	12	8	10	24	16	16
FRIDAY	14	15	9	12	28	6

ARRANGEMENT OF DATA

15 The data should be stored in the table in a logical order. For instance, the following re-arrangement of a previous table would be very confusing.

	TUE	FRI	WEDS	THUR	SAT	MON
TILL 1	110.50	134.26	150.60	145.18	185.70	120.60
TILL 2	104.23	108.14	110.05	99.97	123.40	98.46

SPACE FOR CALCULATED DATA

16 Many times, after data has been entered into a table, some preliminary calculations have to be made. For example, a particular column may require a total of all its entries to be calculated. The result of such a calculation is best embodied within the table so sufficient space should be allotted to it. The following table records the weights of fish delivered by a wholesaler during a week.

	WHITE FISH (Kg)	LOBSTER (Kg)	PRAWNS (Kg)	TOTAL (Kg)
MON	123	20	16	159
TUE	140	32	18	190
WEDS	165	23	20	208
THUR	104	14	15	133
FRI	90	60	17	176
TOTAL	622	149	86	857

The number in the bottom right hand corner is the GRAND TOTAL and is a check that all the earlier additions are correct. It is obtained by adding all the totals above it. This should then be the same as the sum of all the totals to the left of the grand total.

HEADERS AND FOOTERS

17 Every Table needs to have a HEADER that contains a TITLE. The title should be concise yet not so brief that it does not convey the essence of what the table contains.

Every Table need a FOOTER underneath it. This footer should contain;

> **Description**
> **Explanation**
> **Keys**
> **Sources**

DESCRIPTION

18 The description of the contents of the table should always be included in the footer if the title is not adequate.

EXPLANATION

19 Sometimes certain data need to be accompanied by an explanation. This is done in the footer. For example,

RECORD OF EGGS LAID

	HEN 1	HEN 2	HEN 3
WEEK 1	7	2	7
WEEK 2	6	4	8
WEEK 3	6	6	1 *
WEEK 4	6	7	0 *

* HEN 3 Died during week 3

KEYS

20 A KEY is a list of explanations of abbreviations or symbols used in the table. The following table records the sales of Personal Computers by a Company during the month of March.

Personal Computer	1	2	3	4
Number Sold	5	7	10	12

```
KEY   1:  IBM PC XT
      2:  Apricot PC
      3:  Honeywell PC AP
      4:  Amstrad PC
```

SOURCES

21 There are occasions when the title and the description of the data do not adequtely explain where the data was obtained. This is especially so if the data was obtained from a source of Promary Data. In a situation such as this the source of the data should be given in the footer.

TYPES OF REFERENCE TABLE

22 There are various types of table, each serving its own purpose. We shall briefly describe some of the more common ones here. They are;

> **Simple Tables**
> **Complex Tables**
> **Summary Tables**
> **Cross Tabulation Tables**
> **Contingency Tables**
> **Time Series Tables**
> **Frequency Tables**
> **Cumulative Frequency Tables**

SIMPLE TABLES

These tables consist of just one or two columns.

COMPLEX TABLES

These are tables with three or more columns

SUMMARY TABLES

These tables contain calculations made on the data and are used to assist in the analysis of tabulated data.

CROSS TABULATION TABLES

These tables have totals made jointly with respect to two or more methods of classification. For example, row totals and column totals both included.

CONTINGENCY TABLES

These tables allow us to form some conlusion regarding the relationships between the data that is entered within them.

TIME SERIES TABLES

These show the values of the data attributes over a period of time. We shall be saying more about time series later on.

FREQUENCY TABLES

23 We met FREQUENCY TABLES in Chapter 4 of Section 1. The FREQUENCY of a datum is the number of times that particular datum appears in the data. A FREQUENCY TABLE is a table of such frequencies. The following data represents the scores obtained by 50 people throwing 3 darts each at a dartboard.

DARTBOARD SCORES

16	34	19	27	18	17	15	9	53	7
60	48	37	23	22	2	0	15	47	58
18	28	21	51	19	12	60	12	11	34
41	52	27	31	18	9	1	58	15	17
6	4	49	36	27	54	59	18	8	11

We can now group these numbers into intervals and count the number of people who obtained a score within each interval. The intervals are;

$$0 - 20$$
$$21 - 40$$
$$41 - 60$$

By counting the scores we can construct the following table

Frequency Table of Dartboard Scores

	Score Interval		
	0 – 20	21 – 40	41 – 60
Number Scoring	25	12	13

Because this table contains frequencies as its entries it is called a FREQUENCY TABLE.

CUMULATIVE FREQUENCY TABLE

24 A CUMULATIVE FREQUENCY table is derived from a frequency table and contains the successive sums of the frequencies - the ACCUMULATED FREQUENCIES. For example, the previous frequency table can be used to generate the following CUMULATIVE FREQUENCY TABLE.

Cumulative Frequencies of Scores

	Score Interval		
	0 – 20	0 – 40	0 – 60
Number Scoring	25	37	50

The entries are obtained by successive addition of the frequencies. The last entry is, of course, the total number of players - the SUM OF ALL THE FREQUENCIES.

SUMMARY

25 Tables are used to record the measures or descriptions of data attributes obtained in the first part of a statistical enquiry. Such tables are called Reference Tables and they form the basis upon which future analysis of the data will be formed. Because such tables have to be read accurately there are a collection of rules to follow when constructing a clear, readable table. Fundamentally, a table is of columnar construction with the data clearly separated from the descriptive headings. All tables should be headed by a title and accompanied by footnotes to indicate to what the data refers. Second hand data should always be aknowledged by giving the sources. There are various types of reference table.

> **Simple Tables**
> **Complex Tables**
> **Summary Tables**
> **Cross Tabulation Tables**
> **Contingency Tables**
> **Time Series Tables**
> **Frequency Tables**
> **Cumulative Frequency Tables**

KEY POINTS TO NOTE

26 Data attributes, Reference tables, Demonstration tables, Table construction, Types of table, Frequency table, Cumulative frequencies

STUDENT SELF TESTING

SELF REVIEW QUESTIONS

1. Distinguish between Measureable and Descriptive attributes. (3.6)

2. Distinguish between Discrete and Continuous attributes. (4,5)

3. Distinguish between Reference and Demonstration tables. (8-9)

4. List the elements of table construction. (10-16)

5. What do headers and footers contain? (17-21)

6. What is a key? (20)

7. List 7 types of table. (22)

8. What are Frequency and Cumulative frequency tables? (23,24)

EXERCISES (Answers begin on Page 249)

1 Write short notes on the following contrasts;

        a) Measureable and Descriptive attributes
        b) Discrete and Continuous attributes
        c) Reference and Demonstration tables

2 A football team scored 2,1,3,0,0,1,0,2,0 goals in its first nine matches this season. Show this information in a table, with a heading and clear labelling.

RSA 1985

3 Describe briefly the elements of table construction.

4 An hotel group has 200 hotels. 70 are standard grade, 80 are superior grade and the remainder are luxury grade. 40 of the hotels are in the North, 80 are in the South, 50 are in the East and the remainder are in the West. Of the luxury grade hotels, 30 are in the South, 10 are in the East and 5 are in the West. Of the superior grade hotels 35 are in the South, 20 are in the East and 10 are in the West.

Construct a table to display this information.   **LCCI 1984**

5 Secondary Data

INTRODUCTION

1 This Chapter covers the use of Secondary Data. The handling of secondary data is illustated by example.

There are four major parts to this Chapter. They are;

> **Secondary Data**
> **Handling Secondary Data**
> **Limitations Of Secondary Data**
> **Benefits of Secondary Data**

SECONDARY DATA

2 Secondary data is data that is collected from primary data. Primary data is data that is collected first hand and is very costly to obtain. Primary data is published in various journals and is made generally avaiable as a source of data for further analysis. When abstracting data from these sources of primary data to make further analysis one is gathering secondary data.

HANDLING SECONDARY DATA

3 When handling secondary data there are a number of features that must be taken into account. These consist of;

> **Selection For Specific Purposes**
> **Extraction**
> **Preliminary Reference Table**
> **Historical Records**
> **Adjusting Tables**
> **Geberating Summary Figures**
> **Simplifying Tables**

SELECTION FOR SPECIFIC PURPOSES

4 Having decided on the question that one is asking the various sources of primary data must be searched to find data that will be available for secondary use. Generally, primary data will have been collected for a specific purpose and you must make sure that this purpose fits your desired use of it. For example, if you wished to calculate statistics related to the alcohol consumption of the country's population you may also wish to see if men's habits differed significantly from women's habits. In this case you would require a source of data that had been collected on this issue and took men and women into account separately. If men and women were treaeted together then the data would be of little use In your exercise. Make sure that your purposes match as near as possible the original purposes of the primary collection.

EXTRACTION

5 In order to extract data from a primary source we must be practised in the art of reading primary data. The following table shows the number of unemployed people in January, April, July and October of 1984.

UNEMPLOYMENT '000s   (Age and Duration)

Age (yrs)		Under 25				25-54			
Duration (wks)		-26	26-52	52-	All	-26	26-52	52-	All
MALE	Jan	390.2	142.4	238.2	770.8	428.5	185.1	555.2	1169
	April	310.8	176.0	238.8	725.7	387.1	195.4	569.1	1152
	July	342.7	153.4	239.4	735.5	357.7	190.8	577.9	1126
	Oct	417.5	118.7	245.2	781.4	375.4	177.3	581.0	1144
FEMALE	Jan	264.5	95.4	108.9	485.0	187.0	92.2	115.0	394
	April	219.4	124.9	110.5	454.9	187.4	100.6	121.3	410
	July	243.8	110.6	113.5	467.9	182.0	100.2	127.7	410
	Oct	302.0	82.0	120.9	504.9	202.8	87.7	136.0	427

The table consists of 8 rows and 8 columns of data. The rows are in two blocks of 4 rows each. The first 4 rows relate to unemployed men and the second 4 rows relate to unemployed women. The columns are in 2 groups, each group relating to people

Under 25 years old
25 - 54 years old

Within each of these two groups there are 3 columns relating to people unemployed for

> **Up to 26 weeks**
> **26 - 52 weeks**
> **Over 52 weeks**

The fourth column, headed **ALL** in each group of columns gives the total unemployed in each age group.

The data entered in the table represents the number of unemployed people in thousands. For example, the number **142.4** is in the first row and second column. This reads as;

> **In January 1984 there were 142.4 thousand (142,4000) men under 25 who were unemployed and had been so for between 26 and 52 weeks.**

Let us assume that we wish to consider the month of January only. From the above table we have to extract the figures relating to the month of January and insert them into a preliminary reference table.

PRELIMINARY REFERENCE TABLE

6 The table is constructed according to the rules discussed in Chapter 4 of this Section. The following table is produced after extracting the data from the original table.

UNEMPLOYMENT '000s   (Age and During January)

Age (yrs)	Under 25				25-54			
Duration (wks)	-26	26-52	52-	All	-26	26-52	52-	All
MALE	390.2	142.4	238.2	770.8	428.5	185.1	555.2	1169
FEMALE	264.5	95.4	108.9	485.0	187.0	92.2	115.0	394

HISTORICAL RECORDS

7 Sometimes we may wish to consider an historical record over a number of years. In such a situation we should have to locate the same primary source published in previous years. From all these past tables we could then compile an histrical record.

ADJUSTING TABLES

8 Many primary data tables may not be in the same form as we wish to consider. For example, a primary table may contain lengths of nails and screws held in stock by a hardware shop. If the lengths of the nails are measured in inches and the lengths of the screws in millimeters then comparing sizes will require one unit to be converted to the other. For example

Stock Sizes	
NAILS (inches)	SCREWS (mm)
0.5	12.5
1.0	25
1.25	30
1.5	40
2.0	50
2.5	60

This table is now converted to metric units where 25.4 millimeters = 1 inch. The adjusted table is then

Stock Sizes	
NAILS (mm)	SCREWS (mm)
12.7	12.5
25.4	25
31.8	30
38.1	40
50.8	50
63.5	60

Sometimes data may need to be combined. For example, the following table shows the numbers of boys and girls in a local Primary school during the last four years.

Enrollment		
YEAR	BOYS	GIRLS
1984	270	160
1985	288	184
1986	295	191
1987	287	215

If we do not wish to treat boys and girls separately then we shall have to combine the numbers as given in the following table.

Enrollment	
YEAR	PUPILS
1984	430
1985	472
1986	486
1987	502

GENERATING SUMMARY FIGURES

9 Having extracted the data from the primary source we shall almost certainly be required to calculate

> **Totals**
> **Ratios**
> **Percentages**

These are called SUMMARY figures or SECONDARY STATISTICS. To accomodate these summary figures sufficient space will have to be reserved in the reference table.

TOTALS

10 Totals can be COLUMN TOTAL, ROW TOTALS or combinations of both called CROSS TOTALS. The following table records the number of Personal Computers sold by region last year;

Personal Computer Sales By Region				
	North	Midlands	South	TOTAL
Micro PC	520	100	850	1470
Micro PCXP	410	150	904	1464
Micro PCAP	240	60	632	932
Micro 386	45	8	115	168
TOTAL	1215	318	2501	4034

The coumn of totals on the right consist of TOTALS BY TYPE OF MICRO. The totals on the bottom row consist of TOTALS BY REGION. The last number in the bottom righ hand corner is the GRAND TOTAL or CROSS TOTAL that is CROSS TABULATED by adding the column totals or adding the row totals. The fact that these last two sums are the same provides a check that the intermediate totals are correct. Notice that the TOTALS are separated from the main body of the data by bold lines. This shows that the totals are distinct from the original data.

RATIOS

11 The RATIO of the two numbers 5 and 6 is 5 divided by 6. that is 5 ÷ 6. In many instances ratios will be required. For example. the ratio of dogs to cats or the ratio of red apples to green apples. The following table records the ratios of coloured marbles in a marble collection.

Marble Collection					
	BLUE	GREEN	YELLOW	RED	TOTAL
NUMBER	12	8	10	20	50
RATIO	12/50	8/50	10/50	20/50	100%

PERCENTAGES

12 A PERCENTAGE is a ratio where the bottom number is 100. For example, 24 ÷ 100 is called 24 percent and is written as

$$24\%.$$

Any ratio can be converted to a percentage by MULTIPLYING the ratio by 100. For example 2 ÷ 5 becomes

$$(2 \div 5) \times 100 = 200 \div 5$$
$$= 40 \text{ percent OR } 40\%$$

The table recording colours of marbles can be rewritten as a table of percentages as follows;

Marble Collection					
	BLUE	GREEN	YELLOW	RED	TOTAL
NUMBER	12	8	10	20	50
RATIO	24%	16%	20%	40%	100%

SIMPLIFYING TABLES

13 Many primary tables will be required to be simplified, especially if the resulting secondary table is to be used for demonstration purposes. There are three distinct ways of doing this;

> **Rounding**
> **Significant Figures**
> **Re-Ordering**

ROUNDING

14 If we were to ask a plumber for a verbal estimate to install a number of heating radiators in our home he would work out roughly what each part of the job would cost. Adding these together he would arrive at an approximate cost. The cost may be ROUNDED to the nearest £10 or £100. For example,

> **£283 rounded to the nearest £10 is £280,**

we ROUND DOWN because £283 is NEARER to £280 than it is to £290, whereas

> **£283 rounded to the nearest £100 is £300,**

we ROUND UP because £283 is NEARER to £300 than it is to £200.

The effect of rounding is to produce a number that is approximate to the original. In our example the first number is LESS than the original and the second is GREATER. In either case the result is approximate.

If the number to be rounded is exactly halfway between being rounded up and rounded down we agree to round up. For example,

> **£250 rounded to the nearest £100 is £300.**

SIGNIFICANT FIGURES

15 Sometimes a decimal number has too many digits in it for practical use. This problem can be overcome by rounding off to a specified number of SIGNIFICANT FIGURES by discarding digits. The Rule is;

If the digit to be discarded is greater than or equal to 5 then add one to the previous digit. Otherwise the previous digit is unchanged. When discarding digits do it one at a time reading from the rightmost digit.

For example, the number **12.345**

> a) correct to 4 significant figures is **12.35**

Discarding a 5 causes 1 to be added to the 4

> b) correct to 3 significant figures is **12.4**

Discarding a 5 causes 1 to be added to the 3

c) correct to 2 significant figures is **12**

Discarding the 4 leaves the 2 unchanged.

RE-ORDERING

16 Sometimes the data in the original primary data table is displayed in an order that is inappropriate for our purposes. In such a case we can always re-arrange the order in which the data appears. In the historical table that records the number of unemployed men and women the men are listed first followed by the women. If we wish to produce a table that compares men with women it would be more easily read if the numbers of unemployed men and women were side by side. We demonstrate this with the following re-ordered table.

UNEMPLOYMENT '000s (Age and Duration)

Jan 1984	Under 25 yrs old		25 - 54 yrs old	
DURATION	MALE	FEMALE	MALE	FEMALE
0-26 weeks	390.2	264.5	428.5	187.0
26-52 weeks	142.4	95.4	185.1	92.2
52- weeks	238.2	108.9	555.2	115.0
TOTAL	770.8	468.8	1168.8	394.2

LIMITATIONS OF SECONDARY DATA

17 Secondary data is limited simply because it is second-hand. When the original primary data was collected it was done so for a specific purpose. As a result, certain conditions may have been imposed on the population from which the data was gathered. For example, the data may have been gathered from a sample in which case it would be important to know how the sample was selected and how large it was relative to the population from which it was drawn.

The primary data may also have been processed by taking averages of raw data or by rounding the raw data to a number of significant figures. If the extent to which this has been done is not known then the primary data could be an inappropriate source of secondary data.

BENEFITS OF SECONDARY DATA

18 There is a vast amount of primary data on a large variety of subjects. This makes secondary data relatively cheap to obtain. As a result, if the limitations can be quantified and reduced to a minimum then secondary data can be an important and low-cost source of information.

SUMMARY

19 Secondary data is second-hand data in that it comes from a source of primary data. Having decided upon the question to be answered we must select the appropriate primary data to be our source of secondary data. The data is then gleaned from the primary data by entering it into a preliminary reference table. It may already be in tabular form in which case this will form our reference table. Otherwise our reference table will consist of selected items from the original table. Should we require an historical record then we shall have to locate the previous years' editions of our primary source. The primary data may not be in the same units that we require in which case we shall have to adjust the appropriate data. We shall probably be required to produce summary figures from the data. These will consist of totals, ratios and percentages. In many cases we may wish to further manipulate the data by rounding to a secified number of significant figures or by re-arranging the order in which the original data is displayed.

Secondary data is limited because it may have been gathered as primary data for a purpose different from its use as a secondary source. It may also have been manipulated to such an extent that it becomes inappropriate for our uses. It does, however, have the benefit of being quite cheap to obtain.

KEY POINTS TO NOTE

20 Secondary data, Handling secondary data, Summary figures, Rounding, Significant figures, Limitations and benefits.

STUDENT SELF TESTING

SELF REVIEW QUESTIONS

1. What is Secondary data? (2)

2. List the features of handling data. (3)

3. What is a preliminary reference table? (6)

4. What are secondary statistics? (9)

5. List three summary figures. (9)

6. What is a ratio? (11)

7. What is a percentage? (12)

8. What is meant by rounding? (14)

9. What is meant by rounding to a set number of significant figures? (15)

10. Why is secondary data limited? (17)

11. What are the benefits of secondary data? (18)

EXERCISES (Answers begin on Page 249)

1 Explain the meaning of the terms;

> a) Primary Data
> b) Secondary Data

and state some advantages and disadvantages of using each.   **LCCI 1985**

2 Explain the difference between

> a) secondary data
> b) secondary statistics

3 "Sources of secondary data should always be reviewed before deciding to collect Primary Data".

Comment on this statement.

4 The following table shows the number of deliveries made quarterly by a haulage company over the past four years.

DELIVERY RECORD	1984	1985	1986	1987
January/March	1135	1403	1342	1080
April/June	1024	1241	1209	989
July/ September	948	1127	1057	1204
October/December	1236	973	1108	1062

Construct a table of secondary data that records data for the year 1986 only. Include in the table the annual total and the quarterly percentages of that total. Round your data to the nearest 10 deliveries.

5 What are the limitations and benefits of secondary data?

6 Complete the following table;

Frequencies of Scores

	SCORE					
	1	2	3	4	5	TOTAL
Number	8	12	7	13	10	
%						

6 Graphical Representation Of Data

INTRODUCTION

1 This Chapter covers the elementary aspects of constructing a graph. Discrete and Continuous graphs are distinguished and various types of graph are considered. Finally, the mechanics of constructing a graph are described.

There are five major parts to this Chapter. They are;

>Elements Of Graph Construction
>Discrete Graphs
>Continuous Graphs
>Types of Graph
>The Mechanics of Graph Construction

ELEMENTS OF GRAPH CONSTRUCTION

2 The elements of graph construction separate into the following five parts;

>Relationships
>Graphs
>Constructing A Graph
>Plotting The Data
>Using The Graph

RELATIONSHIPS

3 The amount of petrol used by a car is RELATED to the distance the car is driven. The MORE the car is driven the MORE petrol that is used. This last sentence is a verbal description of the RELATIONSHIP between the distance travelled and the petrol used. This RELATIONSHIP between distance travelled and the amount of petrol used can also be described using numbers. This is done in the following table.

Distance (Miles)	30	60	90	120	150
Petrol Used (Gallons)	1	2	3	4	5

Clearly, the greater the distance travelled the more petrol is used. Here we have described the relationship more precisely by describing it with numbers. This RELATIONSHIP can also be described pictorially by drawing a GRAPH of the data.

GRAPHS

4 A GRAPH is a diagram that displays the relationship between two sets of numbers. To illustrate this we shall draw the graph of the relationship described in the last table. The two sets of numbers represent the distance travelled and the corresponding petrol used.

CONSTRUCTING A GRAPH

5 To construct a graph we firstly draw two AXES. Each AXIS is a straight line. The two axes are drawn at right angles to each other. The distance travelled is marked off on the horizontal axis and the petrol used is marked off on the vertical axis as shown in the following diagram.

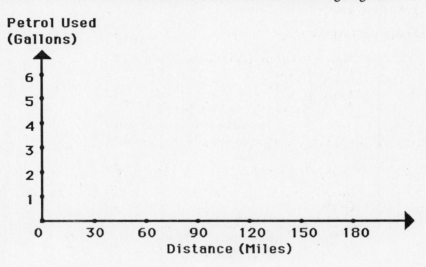

Notice the following important features;

      The Arrows on each axis. These show the direction in which the numbers

      INCREASE

      The axes meet at their COMMON ZERO points

      Each axis is given a clear label describing what the numbers marked off refer to.

What we have done so far is to construct a FRAMEWORK against which we shall next PLOT THE DATA.

PLOTTING THE DATA

6 Consider the first pair of corresponding numbers in the table. These are the distance 30 miles and the quantity of petrol 1 Gallon. This pair of related numbers is now PLOTTED AS A SINGLE POINT as follows;

> **Draw a VERTICAL line through the 30 miles point on the horizontal axis**
>
> **Draw a HORIZONTAL line through the 1 Gallon point on the vertical axis**
>
> **The point where these two lines MEET is then the PLOT of this pair of numbers.**

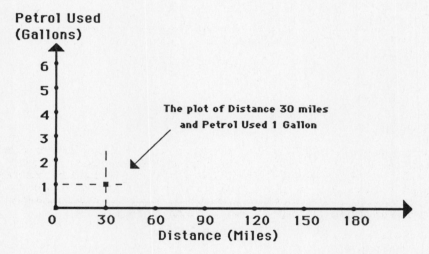

In this way we can plot all the related pairs of numbers in the table. This is done in the following diagram.

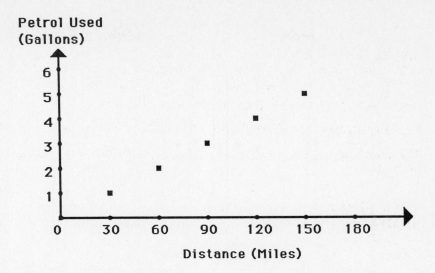

USING THE GRAPH

7 The graph that we have plotted consists of just 5 isolated points. This is because we only have 5 pairs of related numbers in the table. Since a car can travel other distances than those included in the table we could have obtained other related pairs of numbers. These also could then have been plotted on the graph. to cover for all these other possible pairs of related numbers we look closely at the graph that we have drawn. We can see that it is possible to draw a straight line that passes through all the points plotted and this is done in the following diagram.

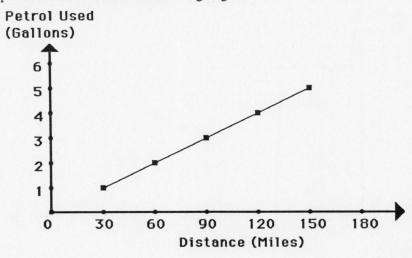

113

Using this straight line we can READ OFF intermediate values for distance and the related value of petrol. For example, if the car travelled for 135 miles it would use 4.5 Gallons of petrol. This is illustrated in the following diagram.

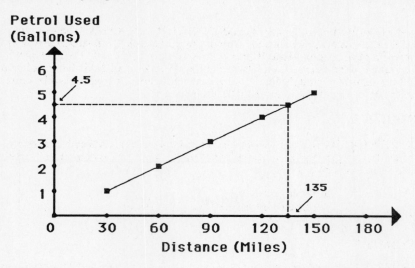

8 Finding INTERmediate values in this way is called INTERPOLATING the data. If we now EXTEND the straight line outside the original data points we can read off values for distance and related petrol used beyond the extremes of the the data. For example, if the car travelled 180 miles it would use 6 Gallons of petrol. Also. if the car did not travel at all it would use no petrol - the 0 miles distance corresponds to the 0 Gallons of petrol used. This is illustrated in the following diagram.

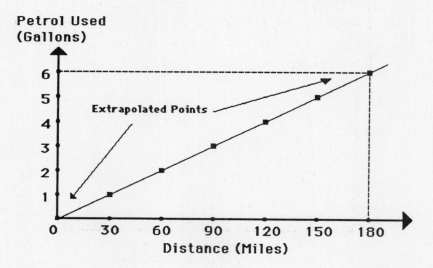

Finding EXtended values in this way is called EXTRAPOLATING the data.

WARNING

9 It is essential that we realize that certain ASSUMPTIONS were made when we interpolated and extrapolated the data. We assumed that the **amount of petrol used for distance travelled follows the same pattern that the original data displays**. This may not be correct. For example, if we made a further observation of the car and found that travelling 45 miles used 1.25 Gallons of petrol then this point would not lie on our straight line. In this case our assumption would not be correct in which case we could not join up the points by a single straight line.

DISCRETE GRAPHS

10 A DISCRETE GRAPH is a graph where the plotted points are all isolated from one another. The 5 points plotted for distance travelled against petrol used is an example of a discrete graph. We shall consider two types of discrete graph.

Scattergraphs
Frequency Graphs For Ungrouped Data

SCATTERGRAPHS

11 In a scattergraph the individual points are scattered over the graph. The scatter may show a regular relationship as it did in our previous example graph or it may show no relationship at all. For example, the following data, when plotted just appear as points randomly located on the graph.

Number Of Coins In My Pocket	1	2	3	4	5
Daily Temperature (Celcius)	2	1	5	4	2.5

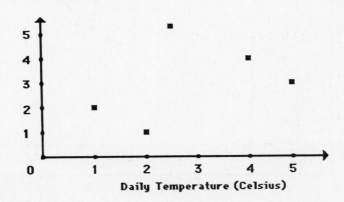

115

There is no relationship between the number of coins I have in my pocket and the temperature and this fact is shown by the randomly scattered points in the graph. There is no way that we could join up the points with a line to allow us to predict the daily temperature from the number of coins in my pocket.

FREQUENCY GRAPHS FOR UNGROUPED DATA

12 A frequency graph of ungrouped data is a scattergraph with the addition of vertical lines. For example, a coin was tossed five times and the number of heads were counted. This was repeated 25 times and the data recorded as follows.

Record of number of HEADS in 25 sets of 5 tosses of a coin

```
1  2  3  3  5
4  3  2  1  4
2  5  4  1  3
3  2  1  1  2
5  4  3  3  2
```

Frequency Table

Number of Heads	1	2	3	4	5
Frequency of Occurrence	5	6	7	4	3

This table of frequencies is plotted in the following diagram to form a scattergraph.

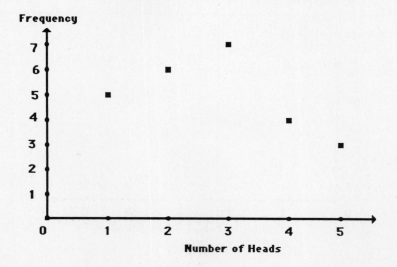

116

Isolated points such as these are somewhat indistinct. In order to highlight the plotted points we add vertical lines to the graph as shown in the following diagram. This is done to give a better visual impression of the relative sizes of the frequencies.

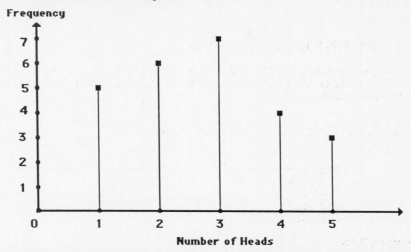

13 These vertical lines are nothing to do with the graph, they are there purely as a guide to the eye. Such vertical lines are distinctive features of frequency graphs for UNGROUPED data. Before we can construct a frequency graph for GROUPED data we must consider CONTINUOUS GRAPHS.

CONTINUOUS GRAPHS

14 A CONTINUOUS GRAPH is a graph that consists of plotted points where the points merge into one another to form an unbroken line or curve. It is, however, impossible to PLOT a continuous graph as it would require the plotting of an infinity of points. The way that a continuous graph is obtained is by plotting isolated points and then joining them up by a line or a curve. We did this when drawing the straight line on the graph illustrating the relationship between petrol used and distance travelled. As a further example consider a growing child. The child's height can be measured every month or every year and these recorded points plotted on a graph. Since the child grows continuously as time passes we can join up the plotted points with a continuous curve and so reasonably represent the relationship between the child's height and age AT ANY TIME. This is the principle of constructing a continuous graph.

We shall now consider two specific types of continuous graphs.

Jagged Line Graphs
Histograms

JAGGED LINE GRAPHS

15 There are many times when it is desireable for reasons of clarity to draw a continuous graph when in fact the data is discrete. For example, the frequency graph that we constructed before just by using the isolated points obtained is not a very clear graph. One way to increase clarity was to draw in vertical bars as we did. An alternative method is to simply join up the individual points of the graph with straight lines.

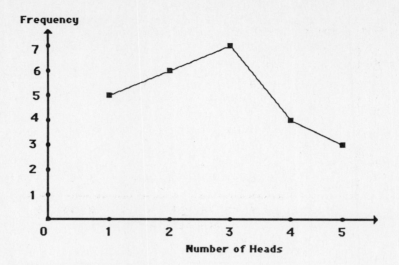

In this way we obtain a continuous JAGGED LINE graph. Again, the lines are there purely to aid in the visual clarification of the picture. This sort of graph where the frequency plots have been joined by straight lines is called a FREQUENCY POLYGON. A POLYGON is any shape that is composed of straight lines.

16 Another example of a jagged line graph is a TIME SERIES GRAPH. A TIME SERIES is a collection of data recorded over a period of time. If we measured the rainfall in our backyard in millimetres each month over the period of a year we might end up with the following table of observations.

MONTH	1	2	3	4	5	6	7	8	9	10	11	12
RAIN (mm)	2	3	0	1	4	2	8	6	3	0	1	2

This data is referred to as a TIME SERIES. We now construct a graph of the time series by plotting the time (in months) on the horizontal axis and the corresponding rainfall (in millimetres) on the vertical axis. This gives the following graph;

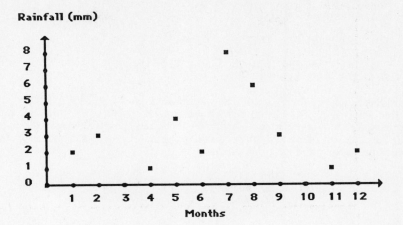

The pattern of this graph is not at all clear as it stands. To bring out the pattern we join each of the isolated points to its neightbour with a straight line.

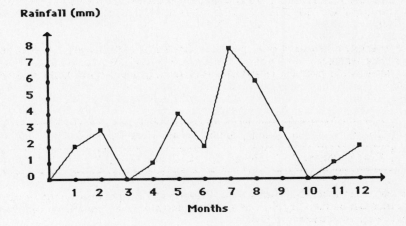

This TIME SERIES graph is a further example of a JAGGED LINE graph.

HISTOGRAM

17 The HISTOGRAM is a continuous graph that is constructed from discrete data where the data has been GROUPED. This is best illustrated with an example. In the following table the daily takings from a shop is recorded over the period of a month (24 working days).

Daily Takings (£)

101	152	180	179	116	158
210	123	223	292	172	155
251	161	234	196	168	242
204	173	145	185	287	208

Plotting a discrete frequency graph of this data would be pointless. Since all the takings are different each has a frequency of 1. The resulting graph would then consist of 24 points all equally distant from the horizontal axis. To gain more information about how the takings vary with number of days we GROUP the data. In the data the lowest takings were £101 and the highest were £292. We decide to break this range into four groups, namely

£100 - £149.99
£150 - £199.99
£200 - £249.99
£250 - £300

We next count the number of days that fall into each group to obtain the FREQUENCIES of days corresponding to each group of takings. By checking against the above table of figures you can see that the following result ensues.

TAKINGS GROUP	FREQUENCY
£100 - £149.99	4
£150 - £199.99	11
£200 - £249.99	6
£250 - £300	3

We now wish to construct a graph of this latter table of calculated frequencies. On the horizontal axis we plot our takings and on the vertical axis we plot the number of days that fall into each class. For example we have 11 days where the takings were between £150 and £199.99. Instead of just plotting a point we draw a horizontal line to represent this fact. At the ends of the line we draw vertical lines down to the horizontal axis. This rectangular box then represents the fact that in 11 of the 24 days the takings were between £150 and £199.99.

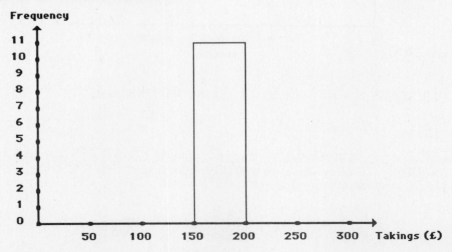

We proceed in this way to plot all the data and finish up with the following graph.

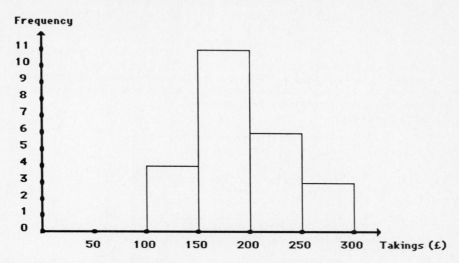

This type of graph is called a HISTOGRAM. It shows us immediately that the class of takings £150 - £199.99 occured more frequently than any other. We shall say more about this in the next Section.

TYPES OF GRAPH

18 There are various other types of graph that are possible for representing data. Those that we shall consider here are;

> **Single Line Graphs**
> **Multiple Graphs**
> **Cumulative Graphs**
> **The Lorentz Curve**

SINGLE LINE GRAPHS

19 The single line graph consists of just ONE line. We have already discussed many of these before so no more will be said except to note that they can used whenever two set of data are to be plotted.

MULTIPLE GRAPHS

20 Multiple graphs contain more than one line and can take one of two forms,

> **Band Charts**
> **Multiple Line Charts**

BAND CHARTS

21 A Band Chart is a graph that contains more than one line and where the areas between the lines are shaded or coloured. They are sometimes called LAYER charts for obvious reasons. The following graph shows the percentages of households in Great Britain who had use of 0, 1, 2 or more cars for the years 1961 to 1985. The three graphs are plotted ON TOP OF EACH OTHER. For example, the line that represents those who had use of no car is the base line for those who had 1 car. The percentages of those who had 1 car are plotted up from the first curve. The graph shows that the percentages of those who had no car decreased between 1961 and 1985 whereas those who had 1 car or 2 or more cars both increased. Notice that the vertical axis is repeated on the right hand side. This is done to make the resultant graph easier to read,

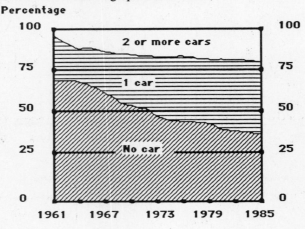

In such a graph the areas must be clearly distinguished and clearly labelled.

MULTIPLE LINE CHARTS

22 In a graph with more than one line, each line is drawn to represent a different set of data, For the sake of clarity each line must be clearly distinguished from each other. This can be simply achieved by drawing the lines in different styles or different colours. In the following graph the prices of three shares have been plotted over a six week period. All three shares are plotted on the same graph.

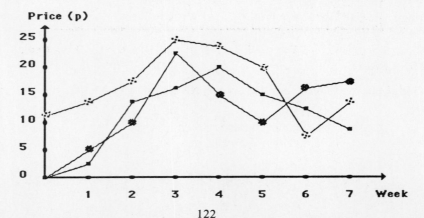

122

In each of the above graphs an explanation will be required to distinguish either different areas or different lines. This can be achieved by using either CAPTIONS on the graph itself or, alternatively, by including an explanatory KEY.

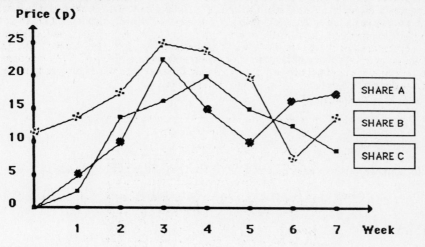

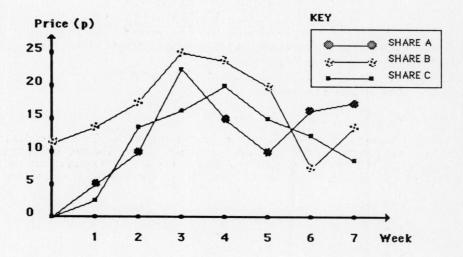

CUMULATIVE GRAPHS

23 A CUMMULATIVE graph is a graph that cummulates the data by SUCCESSIVE ADDITION. For example, a CUMMULATIVE FREQUENCY graph plots the data contained in a frequency table but plots the frequency CUMMULATIVELY. Consider the following frequency table (see paragraph **12**).

Number of Heads In 5 tosses	Frequency in 25 sets
1	5
2	6
3	7
4	4
5	3

From this table we can now construct a CUMMULATIVE FREQUENCY table

Number of Heads In 5 tosses	Cumulative Frequency
1	5
2 or less	11
3 or less	18
4 or less	22
5 or less	25

Here we see that the frequencies have been added - they are CUMMULATIVE. Plotting the data in this latter table we obtain the following graph

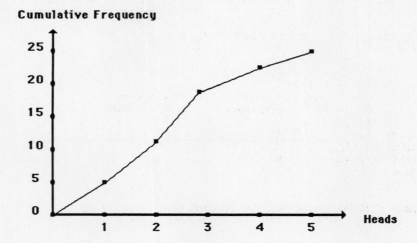

Notice where the points have been plotted. Each point is plotted at the LARGEST end point of the group. For example, in the group **3 or less** the point is plotted at the value of 3 heads. This is because any point TO THE RIGHT OF the number 3 does not satisfy the condition **3 or less** and any point TO THE LEFT of the number 3 cannot include 3 heads. The last point plotted is a recongition of the fact that ALL 25 sets of 5 tosses produced at least one head.

THE LORENTZ CURVE

24 The Lorentz Curve is a graph of cumulative percentages. Typically, a Lorentz Curve could plot the percentage cumulative wealth of a group of people against the cumulative percentage of owners of that wealth. The shape of the graph will display the level of inequality in the distribution of that wealth.

A survey was conducted to find the distribution of wealth amongst a large group of people. The group was divided into 4 categories, each category denoting an income range. The following table records the results of the survey.

	% of Group	% of Wealth
Least paid	10	5
Moderately low paid	30	25
Moderately highly paid	40	30
High paid	20	40

The column headed **% Of Group** contains the percentages that each income category forms of the group. For example, 30% of the group are in the **Moderately low paid** category. Similary, the **% Of Wealth** column contains the percentage of the group's total wealth that is owned by each income category. For example, 25% of the total wealth of the group is owned by the 30% Moderately low paid.

From this table we now construct a cumulative table.

	Cumulative % of Group	Cumulative % Of total wealth
Least paid	10	5
Moderately low paid	40	30
Moderately highly paid	80	60
High paid	100	100

This data is plotted to produce the following graph;

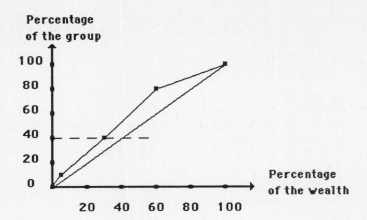

The segmented line is the cumulative frequency polygon otherwise known as the LORENZ CURVE. The single straight line is drawn for comparison purposes. This straight line is the line of EQUAL DISTRIBUTION. For example, the broken horizontal line through 40% of the group to this line reads off 40% of the total wealth. This horizontal cuts the cumulative frequency polygon where the horizontal axis reads 30% of the total wealth. This means that 40% of the group only own 30% of the total wealth. The wealth is not equally distributed over the group. The departure of the polygon from the single straight line indicates the amount of inequality - the greater the gap the greater the inequality of distribution.

THE MECHANICS OF GRAPH CONSTRUCTION

25 The purpose of constructing a graph is to present a picture of the data. In such a way you will be presenting a synopsis and conveying a general visual impression of the data. The graph must be simply, cleanly and clearly constucted. There are four factors to consider to achieve this.

> **Equipment**
> **Axes**
> **Titles, Sources and Footnotes**
> **Finished appearance**

EQUIPMENT

26 Listing equipment may seem trite but unless careful preparations are made beforehand the best end-result will not be produced. The following list of equipment is essential;

> **Sharp Pencil**   : The preliminary graph will be drawn in pencil and then inked over with a pen. For this a sharp pencil is required to make accurate plots. Preferably use an HB pencil.

Eraser   : Obvious but often forgotten. After inking over the pencil plots the pencil marks must be removed using a good quality soft eraser.

Clear Black Pen: The final graph will be produced in black ink using a fine nibbed pen. You may also wish to use a broader nibbed pen to draw in the axes.

Ruler : All straight lines, such as axes, must be drawn with a straight edge. A clear plastic ruler is best as you can see more clearly where you are drawing.

Graph Paper : The final graph must be produced on graph paper. This paper is printed with vertical and horizontal lines to ensure that all the plots are accurately drawn.

Rough Paper : Always have plenty of rough paper on hand for trials. You will have to set the scales and draw a rough graph first before you will know how it will fit onto the final sheet of paper.

AXES

27 Having decided which axis is to be the horizontal axis and which is to be the vertical you must next decide on the SCALE to use for each axis. The scale is the number of small divisions that represent one unit of measurement on the axis. For example, If you have a sheet of graph paper with fifteen centimeters of available space horizontally and the data to be plotted on it is spread between 0 and 150 then each centimeter of axis can represent 10 units of data. This is the SCALE. Always make a point of drawing the largest graph that your sheet of graph paper will allow. When constructing the axes ensure that the available data will be plotted over the full length of the line drawn. There is nothing more ridiculous than a sheet of graph paper where the axes extend to the edge of the paper yet the graph is crammed into one small corner. In order to get the best effect a number of trials will be made in rough before coming to a final conclusion. During this rough phase some particular problems might occur which can be solved by the following considerations.

Zero-ed Scales
Breaks and Pleats

ZERO-ED SCALES

28 Always try to show the ZERO point of your axis. This will then put your plots into perspective. Sometimes, however, it is just not appropriate to show the zero because it will add nothing to the picture. If, for example, you were to plot the price of mutton over the last twelve months there is no virtue in showing the zero on the cost axis. That would not make sense - mutton was never free! In this case the price axis would just cover the range of values. Notice also that it is meaningless to talk of a zero on the horizontal axis.

	Price (£)		Price (£)
Jan	1.20	Jul	1.18
Feb	1.45	Aug	1.21
Mar	1.20	Sep	1.20
Apr	1.10	Oct	1.28
May	0.90	Nov	1.28
Jun	1.11	Dec	1.35

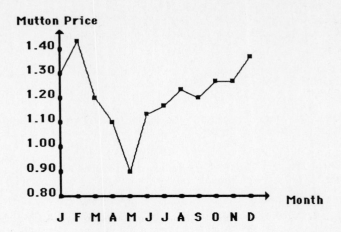

29 Notice that the horizontal scale has MONTHS plotted on it. This is the first time we have not used numbers. We could, of course, have coded the months from 1 to 12 but the notation that we have used is quite adequate.

30 If now we were to plot the marks attained in an examination then the zero point should be included in both axes. It may be that nobody actually scored zero but by putting it in the other plots are put into perspective.

Marks Awarded to a Student for Assessments and Examinations during a Course of Study

Assessment 1	**32**
Assessment 2	**45**
Examination 1	**56**
Assessment 3	**61**
Assessment 4	**65**
Examination 2	**60**

These marks are plotted on the following graph. Notice that the points are joined. This gives a visual impression of the student's progress during the Course.

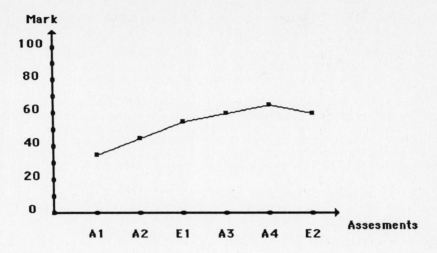

31 Sometimes it may be desireable to put in the zero point but to do so would result in a graph that was crammed into the far corner of the paper. To overcome this effect we insert what are called breaks or pleats.

BREAKS AND PLEATS

32 There are occasions when we wish to construct a multiple line graph

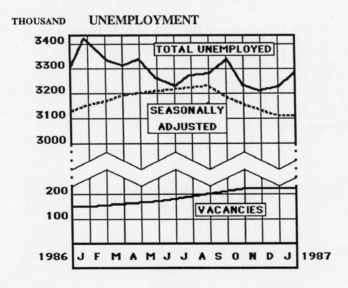

129

where the scales of different lines are widely separated. In such a situation we can resort to using BREAKS in the graph. This is illustrated in the previous graph.

In this graph two of the lines have comparable scales but the third is widely separated from the other two. To accomodate all three lines on the same graph we have resorted to a well indicated break in the graph. Notice also the grid lines are included to make the graph more easy to read.

On other occasions it may be desireable to include the zero but to do so would result in a graph that was compressed to one side. In such a situation it is possible to accomodate the zero by inserting a PLEAT in the appropriate axis. This indicates that a range of values has been omitted. The following graph shows the cumulative frequency of the number of petals on a particular type of flower. The zero is included on the horizontal axis and the pleat indicates that the range 0 to 9 has been omitted. Had we included this range then the graph would have been compressed at the right hand side of the horizontal axis.

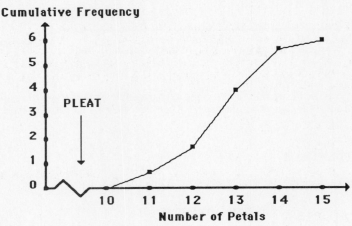

Having decided on the scale and having pencilled in the preliminary axes we now pencil in the axis descriptions. Eventually you will go over this in ink so make sure that the writing is large enough to be clear and distinct yet not so large as to dominate the rest of the graph.

TITLES, SOURCES AND FOOTNOTES

33 When constructing a graph you must remember that it has to have a TITLE at the top and a SOURCE at the bottom indicating the origin of the data. Make sure that enough room is left for these to be inserted. There may also be a need for FOOTNOTES which expain various features of the graph. These are also included at the bottom of the graph - so if you need them make sure there is room for them.

FINISHED APPEARANCE

34 Finally when all the above points have been catered for and the graph has been drawn accurately and neatly in pencil the entire picture is retraced in ink and the extraneous pencil lines erased. All captions and writing that accompanies the graph must be uncluttered yet clearly legible. To finish off the presentation you may wish to enclose the entire graph in a frame. This does give it a compact appearance though it is not necessary.

SUMMARY

35 The detailed relationship between two sets of data becomes more clearly defined when the data is plotted on a graph. The graph is constructed by firstly creating the framework on which the points are plotted. This is usually done in rough with the final version being drawn on graph paper in pencil. Once the data has been plotted and the graph completed it is then overdrawn in ink. All good graphs are annotated with tiles, source and footnotes.

There are two categories of graph, discrete and continuous. A continuous graph is created from a discrete graph by joining the individually plotted points together. A continuous graph may be sufficiently accurate to allow interpolation and extrapolation. There are, however, a collection of continuous graphs that are constructed to aid the eye in reading what is essentially a discrete graph. These are not capable of being used for interpolation or exprapolation. Typical of these graphs are jagged line graphs and histograms.

KEY POINTS TO NOTE

36 Relationships, Graphs, Plotting data, Interpolation, Extrapolation, Discrete graphs, Continuouos graphs, Cumulative graphs, The Lorentz Curve.

STUDENT SELF TESTING

SELF REVIEW QUESTIONS

1. What is a relationship? (3)

2. What is a graph? (4)

3. What are axes? (5)

4. How do you plot data? (6)

5. What is meant by interpolation and extrapolation? (7,8)

6. List 2 types of discrete graph. (10-12)

7. List 2 types of continuous graph. (14-17)

8. List two types of multiple graph. (20-22)

9. What is a cumulative frequency graph? (23)

10. What is a Lorentz Curve? (24)

11. What are Zero-ed scales? (28-31)

12. What are breaks and pleats? (32)

EXERCISES (Answers begin on Page 249)

1 A factory manufactures plasticware. In one section of the factory they produce plastic caps for yoghourt cartons in bulk units of 50,000. The cost of manufacturing these caps are recorded in the following table;

Bulk Units Manufactured	1	2	3
Total Costs (£000's)	1.5	3.0	4.5

a) Plot this data on a graph
b) If possible draw a straight line through the points
c) Can you find out how much 0.5 units would cost?
d) Can you find out how much 4 units would cost?
e) What are the costs involved if no units are manufactured?
f) Comment briefly on any assumptions and your reasoning on obtaining your answers to c), d) and e)

2 For each of the following Datum 1 is plotted on the horizontal axis and Datum 2 is plotted on the vertical axis. For each case plot a scattergraph. Decide whether a relationship exists between Datum 1 and Datum 2 for each case.

a) Datum 1   1   2   3   4
    Datum 2   10   2   5   4

b) Datum 1   1   1.5   2   2.5   3
    Datum 2   1   2.25   4   6.25   9

c) Datum 1   2   4   6   8
    Datum 2   12   8   4   0

3 Two coins were tossed together 30 times. Each time the number of heads were recorded in the following table;

```
1 1 2 2 1 0
1 0 1 0 2 1
2 1 1 2 1 1
1 0 2 1 2 0
0 1 1 2 0 1
```

Construct a frequency table and plot a frequency graph of this data.

4 A self-serve petrol station recorded the number of gallons of petrol purchased during one hour. The data is recorded below;

1.51	8.03	9.00	6.03	4.45	6.80	7.50	1.23	5.87
4.50	7.04	4.00	1.75	5.01	5.22	4.00	2.89	5.46
3.21	7.80	8.60	1.61	7.22	3.03	9.89	2.12	1.40
5.51	4.86	9.50	3.20	6.00	3.65	8.57	7.55	4.44
9.01	1.96	8.00	2.05	7.56	3.57	5.12	4.98	6.65

Construct a grouped frequency table for the groups;

> **0 - 1.9 gallons**
> **2.0 - 3.9 gallons**
> **4.0 - 5.9 gallons**
> **6.0 - 7.9 gallons**
> **8.0 - 9.9 gallons**

Draw a histogram of this data.

5 In a quality control exercise a baker weighed a sample of 100 cakes taken at random from his assembly line. The following table records the findings.

Weight	Number	Weight	Number
19.5	1	23.0	27
20.0	1	23.5	12
20.5	3	24.0	17
21.0	3	24.5	11
21.5	2	25.0	7
22.0	1	25.5	2
22.5	12	26.0	1

Construct a cumulative frequency table and plot a cumulative frequency graph. Display the zero on both axes.

6 A large number of companies were asked for the numbers they employed. The following table records the data.

Number of employees	% of all companies	% of all employees
Up to 49	10	5
50 - 99	20	15
100 - 499	35	35
500 - 999	20	20
1000+	15	25

a) Construct a Cumulative percentage table from this data
b) Plot a Lorentz Curve of the cumulative percentages
c) How equally distributed are the employees over the companies?

Section 4 Deriving The Statistics

This Section deals with the various means whereby a collection of data can be summarized by a collection of statistics. The single statistics of central tendency are considered in the first two Chapters. The multiple statistics of fractiles and index numbers are covered in the following two Chapters. These four Chapters cover the statistics required to adequately summarize data at this level. In the following two Chapters relationships between two sets of data are investigated using regression and correlation. Finally, the use of time series as a method to predict the future course of events is reviewed.

There are seven Chapters in this Section. They are;

1 Single Statistics

INTRODUCTION

1 In this Chapter we consider the role of the single statistic in summarizing data. The single statistics considered are the mean, of which we consider five types, the median and the mode.

There are six major parts to this Chapter. They are;

> **Single Statistics**
> **Central Tendency**
> **Means**
> **Median**
> **Mode**
> **Bi-Modal Data**

SINGLE STATISTICS

2 When presented with a set of data, the objective of the statistician is to reduce the mass of data to a smaller collection of statistics that adequately summarize the entire set of data. Data in the large can be incomprehensible so reducing it to a smaller representative collection of statistics aids in its comprehension. In this chapter we shall be considering processes that reduce data to a SINGLE statistic that measures what is called the CENTRAL TENDENCY of the data.

CENTRAL TENDENCY

3 An ordinary kitchen knife has two central points. One of them is located midway between the two ends of the knife and the other is located at the balance point. The first centre is the geometric centre. The second is the mass centre - when you balance the knife there is as much mass on the left as there is on the right of the balance point. The mass centre will not be in the same place as the geometric centre if the handle is heavier than the blade. In much the same way a collection of data can have different central points. We say that each of these points is a measure of a CENTRAL TENDENCY of the data. The three measures of central tendency that we shall consider in this Chapter are;

> **The Mean**
> **The Median**
> **The Mode**

THE MEAN

4 The MEAN is an AVERAGE and we met one average in Section 1. We say AN average rather than THE average because there are more than one. The average that we met in section one is called the ARITMETIC MEAN. It is defined as the sum of a collection of numbers divided by the number of numbers. For example, the arithmetic mean of the 6 numbers

$$1, 2, 3, 4, 5, 6$$

is

$$(1+2+3+4+5+6) \div 6 = 21 \div 6 = 3.5$$

Notice that the arithmetic mean 3.5 is NOT one of the numbers. This is not always the case. For example, the arithmetic mean of 1,2,3,4,5 is 3, which *is* one of the numbers. We shall now look at four other means;

> **The Weighted Arithmetic Mean**
> **The Progressive Mean Or Moving Average**
> **The Geometric Mean**
> **The Harmonic Mean**

THE WEIGHTED ARITHMETIC MEAN

5 The weighted arithemtic mean is another version of the arithmetic mean. It has the same value as the ordinary arithmetic mean but it is calculated differently. Before adding the numbers they are multiplied by other numbers called WEIGHTS. For example, consider the following collection of 25 numbers

$$
\begin{array}{ccccc}
1 & 5 & 4 & 3 & 1 \\
3 & 2 & 1 & 5 & 2 \\
1 & 4 & 1 & 2 & 4 \\
1 & 4 & 3 & 2 & 3 \\
4 & 1 & 3 & 1 & 5 \\
\end{array}
$$

In this collection there are only 5 DIFFERENT numbers, namely 1, 2, 3, 4 and 5. If we group these numbers together we can construct the following frequency table.

Number	Frequency
1	8
2	4
3	5
4	5
5	3

25 Numbers in total

To calculate the arithmetic average of the 25 numbers we could add them all together and divide by 25. That is;

$$66 \div 25 = 2.64$$

Alternatively, we can first multiply each different number by the number of times it appears - its frequency of occurrence. That is

$$[(1 \times 8) + (2 \times 4) + (3 \times 5) + (4 \times 5) + (5 \times 3)] \div 6 = 66/25 = 2.64$$

The frequencies that multiplied each number are examples of what are called WEIGHTS. We shall see later, when we consider INDEX NUMBERS another use of weights. This weighted arithmetic mean is identical to the arithmetic mean. The arithmetic mean is usually calculated for ungrouped data. The weighted arithmetic mean is calculated when the data is grouped and where the weights are the frequencies of the distinct data items.

The arithmetic mean is the most commonly used measure of average. It is both easily evaluated and understood. It suffers from the fact that it does not necessarily correspond to any single datum. For example, the statement that **'the average family has 2.4 children'** could not possibly be taken to mean that some children come in fractional parts. The arithmetic mean can also be unduly influenced by extreme values. For example 300 number 1's and 1 number 300 have an arithmetic mean of

$$(1 \times 300 + 300) \div 301 = 1.99$$

This average is practically double the average of the 300 number 1's by themselves.

A further disadvantage of the arithmetic mean is that there is no graphical method of obtaining it. This is not the case with either the Median or the Mode which we shall consider later.

PROGRESSIVE MEAN or MOVING AVERAGE

6 The MOVING AVERAGE of a list of data is the arithmetic average of a group of the data calculated successively by moving through the list. Consider the following table of daily rainfall figures taken over a two week period.

RAINFALL (centimeters)

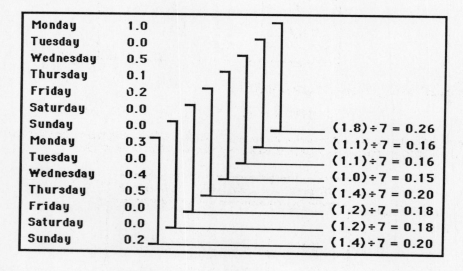

Monday	1.0	
Tuesday	0.0	
Wednesday	0.5	
Thursday	0.1	
Friday	0.2	
Saturday	0.0	
Sunday	0.0	$(1.8) \div 7 = 0.26$
Monday	0.3	$(1.1) \div 7 = 0.16$
Tuesday	0.0	$(1.1) \div 7 = 0.16$
Wednesday	0.4	$(1.0) \div 7 = 0.15$
Thursday	0.5	$(1.4) \div 7 = 0.20$
Friday	0.0	$(1.2) \div 7 = 0.18$
Saturday	0.0	$(1.2) \div 7 = 0.18$
Sunday	0.2	$(1.4) \div 7 = 0.20$

On the second Monday the rainfall of the previous 7 days are averaged to give 0.26mm. The following day this process is repeated - the rainfall of the previous 7 days are averaged to give 0.54mm. This process is repeated for each successive day. In this way we generate the MOVING AVERAGE. Each time the average is calculated we add a datum at one end and subtract a datum from the other. The moving average is sometimes referred to as the PROGRESSIVE MEAN

GEOMETRIC MEAN

7 On Monday morning little James woke up feeling unwell. He complained of two itchy spots on his chin. His mother wrapped him up warm and sent him out to play in the fresh air. By lunchtime his two itchy spots had become six and he had a slight fever. Mother diagnosed chicken pox and sent him to bed with a glass of warm milk and a stack of his favourite comics. He fell asleep quite quickly and when he awoke at tea-time he was the proud owner of 162 spots all over his body. Boy, did he itch!

The point of this story is to introduce the idea of of an AVERAGE RATE OF INCREASE. The 2 spots increased threefold to 6 and then those 6 increased 27-fold to 162. The question we wish to answer is;

What was the average rate of increase? The following table records the actual rates of increase.

Number	Rate Of Increase
2	–
6	3
162	27

The arithmetic average of these two rates of increase is

$$(3 + 27) \div 2 = 15.$$

However, using this average does not work as we can see in the following table where the number of spots is obtained by moving backwards from the average rate of increase of 15.

Number	Rate Of Increase
2	–
30	← 15
450	← 15

The correct average rate of increase is obtained by multiplying the two rates together and then taking the square root of the result.

$$\sqrt{(3 \times 27)} = \sqrt{81} = 9$$

Using this average rate of increase the 2 would increase to 18 and the 18 would increase to 162

Number	Rate Of Increase
2	–
18	⟵——— 9
162	⟵——— 9

Notice that the average rate of increase using the geometric mean gives the final number correctly but does not give the intermediate number correctly.

8 This average is called the GEOMETRIC MEAN. When dealing with RATES OF CHANGE the average rate of change is given by the geometric mean. If there are N numbers to be averaged in this way then the Geometric Mean is the Nth root of their combined product. For example, the Geometric Mean of **1, 2, 4, 8** is

$$\sqrt[4]{(1 \times 2 \times 4 \times 8)} = \sqrt[4]{64} = 2.83$$

HARMONIC MEAN

9 Olivia was due in Birmingham at midday. The journey was 30 miles long but there were delays to be expected. The first ten miles were to be done in heavy morning traffic and an average speed of 10 mph was to be expected. The next ten miles were full of roadworks so an average speed of 20 mph was all that was possible. The last ten miles were clear so she could average 60 mph. On these facts Olivia reckoned that her average speed would be

$$(10 + 20 + 30) \div 3 = 30 \text{ mph.}$$

So it should only take an hour to cover the 30 miles. Olivia left at 11.00 am and was 40 minutes late for her appointment. The following reasoning explains why this was so.

The first 10 miles covered at 10 mph took 1 hour
the next 10 miles covered at 20 mph took 30 minutes
the last 10 miles covered at 60 mph took 10 minutes

The total travelling time = 1 hour 40 minutes

= 5/3 hours

This gives an average speed of

$$\text{Distance} \div \text{Time} = 30 \div (5/3)$$

$$= \textbf{18 mph and NOT 30 mph}$$

Olivia had made the mistake of taking the arithmetic average of the three speeds when in fact she should have taken the HARMONIC AVERAGE. This is obtained by adding the reciprocals of the speeds to give;

$$1/10 + 1/20 + 1/60 = 10/60$$

This sum is then averaged (divided by three) to give

$$(10/60) \div 3 = 10/180 = 1/18$$

This result is then the reciprocal of the average speed. 18 mph is then the HARMONIC AVERAGE of 10 mph, 20 mph and 60 mph each taken over the specified durations. When calculating average speeds over equal distances the HARMONIC MEAN must be used.

THE MEDIAN

10 The MEDIAN is the MIDDLE DATUM. It is that datum that divides the data into two equal parts. For example, the number 19 is the MEDIAN of the seven numbers

$$\textbf{23, 14, 7, 50, 8, 33, 19.}$$

If we rearrange the numbers in ascending order

$$\textbf{7, 8, 14, 19, 23, 33, 50}$$

then we see that the number 19 is the MIDDLE one - the MEDIAN, there are as many numbers below it as there are above it.

Obviously, if there is an odd number of data then the median is the centre datum. If, however, there is an even number of data then there is no middle datum. In this case the Median is taken to be the average of the middle TWO data. For example, in the list of six numbers

$$\textbf{1, 3, 5, 7, 9, 11}$$

there is no single middle number since there is an even number of numbers. The middle two numbers are 5 and 7 and the average of these two numbers is 6. Consequently, the median is 6 even though that number is not one of the data.

It is also possible for more than one datum to have the same value os the median. For example, in the list

$$\textbf{2, 4, 4, 4, 6}$$

the middle 4 is the median.

141

MEDIAN OF GROUPED DATA

11 So far we have considered discrete data where the median is easily located. In the case of grouped data the process is a little more involved. The following table lists the number of items within certain price ranges sold by a local Supermarket. The third column is the accumulated total of the second column. It is called the CUMULATIVE TOTAL.

Price range	Number of Items	Cumulative Total
0.00p - 0.50p	625	625
0.51p - £1.00	882	1507
£1.01 - £1.50	518	2025
£1.51 - £2.00	235	2260
£2.01 - £2.50	87	2347
£2.50 - £3.00	54	2401
TOTAL	**2401**	

The problem is to find the median price. Since there are 2401 items in total, if we ranked all the prices in ascending order the middle one - the median - would be the 1201st on the list.

The 1201st item lies somewhere in the 0.51 - 1.00 group. There are 1507 items in the range 0.00p - £1.00. The first 625 items are in the first group so if we ranked the second group in ascending order the 1201st item will be the

$$(1201 - 625) = \textbf{576th item in this group.}$$

Now, there are 882 items in the second group and the difference in price between the cheapest at 51p and the most expensive at £1.00 is 49p. Consequently, the AVERAGE PRICE DIFFERENCE BETWEEN ITEMS IN THIS GROUP is

$$49 \div 882 = \textbf{1/18 p}$$

In this group the first item costs 51p so the 576th item in this group would be expected to cost,

$$51p + 576 \times (1/18) p = 51p + 32p = 83p$$

The median price is 83p. This is only appproximate because no two items differ in price by the average price difference of 1/18 p. However, without ranking every single price it is the best that we can do.

GRAPHICAL LOCATION OF THE MEDIAN

12 Another effective way of obtaining an accurate approximation is to use the following graphical method. Using the cumulative data we have just handled we can construct the following cumulative frequency graph - which is also referred to as the OGIVE.

142

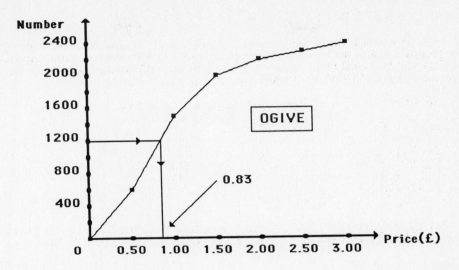

Notice that we have plotted the horizontal points at the highest end points of each interval (see paragraph 23 of Chapter 6, Section 3).

We know that the 1201st item is the median item so drawing a horizontal line from 1201 to the ogive and then drawing the vertical line to the price axis shows us that the price of the 1201 th item is 83p.

THE MODE

13 The last single statistic that we consider in this chapter is the MODE. The MODE is the most fashionable datum - the datum that occurs most frequently.

In a survey of the amounts of money drawn from an automatic teller outside a bank the following usage was recorded over a period of time.

Amount Withdrawn	Number of Withdrawals
£10	12
£20	82
£30	125
£40	74
£50	7

Here we see that more people withdrew £30.00 than any other amount. So £30.00 is the MODE amount.

THE MODAL CLASS FOR GROUPED DATA

14 Sometimes the MODE can be an inappropriate statistic to use when considering ungrouped data. For example, in a History examination 50 students all received different marks so no single mark was obtained by more than one student - there was no MODE. Either that or there were 50 modes! When the data was grouped, however, a different picture appeared. The following table contains the grouped data

Marks Awarded	Number of students
0 - 9	3
10 - 19	4
20 - 29	4
30 - 39	5
40 - 49	8
50 - 59	10
60 - 69	6
70 - 79	4
80 - 89	4
90 - 100	2

Here the 50 - 59 group is the most heavily populated - this is the MODAL GROUP or MODAL CLASS. We display this graphically in the following histogram. The MODAL CLASS is the largest segment of the histogram as is indicated in the diagram.

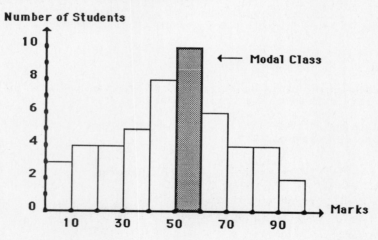

SINGLE MODE FOR GROUPED DATA

15 It is possible to obtain a single mode value for grouped data. We can do this in one of two ways;

Graphically
By Formula

GRAPHICALLY

16 Having obtained the histogram for the grouped data we focus attention on the modal group - the tallest block in the histogram.

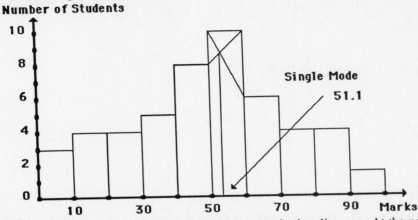

We now draw two diagonal lines within this block as shown in the diagram. At the point where these two line intersect we drop a vertical line to the horizontal axis. The point where this vertical line meets the horizontal axis is then the SINGLE MODE VALUE FOR THE GROUPED DATA.

BY FORMULA

17 It can be shown that the single mode value for grouped data is given by the formula;

$$l_m + c_m(f_m - f_{m-1}) + \{2f_m - (f_{m-1} - f_{m+1})\}$$

where

c_m = the width of the modal group
l_m = the lower value of the modal group
f_m = the frequency of the modal group
f_{m-1} = the frequency of the group to the left of the modal group
f_{m+1} = the frequency of the group to the right of the modal group

In the previous example,

$$
\begin{aligned}
c_m &= 10 \\
l_m &= 50 \\
f_{m-1} &= 8 \\
f_m &= 10 \\
f_{m+1} &= 6
\end{aligned}
$$

so that the SINGLE MODE VALUE is

$$= 50 + 10(10 - 8) \div \{2 \times 10 - (8 - 6)\}$$

$$= 50 + (20 \div 18)$$

$$= 51.1$$

BI-MODAL DATA

18 Though we are only considering single statistics in this Chapter it is appropriate here to mention BI-MODAL data. It is sometimes the case that when drawing a graph to represent data we find TWO PEAKS. For example, the following table records the number of new plant shoots appearing during successive days from two different types of seed.

Day	1	2	3	4	5	6	7	8
Plant A	2	4	20	6	7	8	4	0
Plant B	0	1	2	3	10	24	8	3
Total	2	5	22	9	17	32	12	3

The following graph illustrates this data.

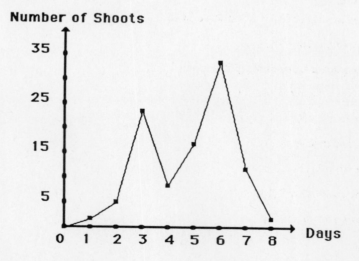

The graph displays two peaks during the 3rd and 6th days. This data is said to possess TWO MODES and is described as being BI-MODAL.

SUMMARY

19 When evaluating a mean to summarize data then care must be taken to select the most appropriate one. The straightforward case of a mean of a list of numbers is called the arithmetic mean. If the data is grouped then the weighted arithmetic mean may be more easily obtained. In the case of an average that is to be taken of a group of data moving successively through a list of data then the moving average is the clear choice. For averaging rates of change we use the geometric mean and for averaging speeds we use the harmonic mean.

Two other means are the median and the mode. The median is the middle datum that divides the data into two equal halves. The mode is the most commonly occuring datum. In the case of grouped data the mode is the group with the largest number of members. Both of these means have the advantage of being obtainable graphically. Sometimes a graph of the data displays two distinct modes. In such a case the data is said to be bi-modal.

KEY POINTS TO NOTE

20 Central tendency, Arithmetic mean, Weighted arithmetic mean, Moving average, Geometric mean, Harmonic mean, Median, Cumulative total, Mode, Modal group. Bi-modal.

STUDENT SELF TESTING

SELF REVIEW QUESTIONS

1. What is meant by CENTRAL TENDENCY? (3)

2. What is the difference between the arithmetic mean and the weighted arithmetic mean? (4,5)

3. List two disadvantages of the arithmetic mean. (5)

4. What is a moving average? (6)

5. When is a geometric mean used? (7,8)

6. When is an harmonic mean used? (9)

7. What is a median? (10)

8. What is a cumulative total? (11)

9. What is the mode? (13)

10. What is the modal class? (14)

11. What is bi-modal data? (18)

EXERCISES (Answers begin on Page 249)

1 Given the set of five numbers;

$$8, \ 3, \ 4, \ 6, \ 2$$

find;

    a) the arithmetic mean
    b) the geometric mean
    c) the harmonic mean
    d) the median

2 Given the set of numbers;

$$1 \ 2 \ 2 \ 3 \ 4 \ 2$$
$$2 \ 1 \ 3 \ 2 \ 4 \ 1$$
$$2 \ 1 \ 1 \ 3 \ 3 \ 4$$
$$1 \ 1 \ 2 \ 4 \ 4 \ 3$$

find

    a) the median
    b) the modal class
    c) the single mode by a graphical method
    d) the single mode by formula

3 A small engineering firm has recorded the bonuses paid to its 11 workshop staff

Bonus week

£13.76 £14.73 £12.98 £9.96 £22.43
£11.69 £12.74 £17.68 £16.93 £17.54
£14.64

    a) Arrange the data in ascending order
    b) What is the median bonus?
    c) Find to the nearest penny the arithmetic mean bonus paid.
    d) Does the arithmetic mean or the median give more information to the employer?

RSA 1986

4 A football team scored **2, 1, 3, 0, 0, 1, 0, 2, 0** goals in its first nine games this season. The mean score in the next 16 games was 1.25. What was the mean for all 25 games?

RSA 1985

5 The ages of the employees of a company are shown in the following table;

Age (years)	Number of employees
15 and under 25	21
25 and under 35	37
35 and under 45	25
45 and under 55	12
55 and under 65	5

a) Calculate the mean, median and mode of the ages.
b) For each of these measures give one advantage and one disadvantage

LCCI 1985

6. A chocolate factory makes chocolate bars that are supposed to weigh 75 grams. A sample of 50 bars from one day's production had the following weights (in grams)

74.9 75.1 75.0 75.0 75.1 75.1 75.0 75.1 74.9 75.5 75.2
75.2 75.0 75.3 75.1 75.3 75.0 74.9 75.0 75.2 74.9 75.0
75.0 75.1 74.9 75.2 75.3 75.4 75.1 75.0 75.0 74.9 75.2
75.2 75.0 75.0 74.9 75.1 75.2 74.9 75.4 75.1 75.3 74.9
75.4 75.1 74.9 75.3 75.3 75.1

a) Show this data in a frequency table

b) If the records were made to the nearest 0.1 gram, what are the exact boundaries of the classes in your table?
c) Illustrate the data in a histogram

d) The median weight is 75.07 grams. Explain which measure, mean or median, you think gives more useful information about the "average" weight of chocolate bars.

RSA 1985

7 On day 1, a grain of rice is placed is on a chessboard square. On day 2, two grains of rice are placed on another square. On day 3, four grains of rice are placed on yet another square. Each successive day twice the number of grains of rice are added than were added the previous day. Show that the three-day moving average also doubles each day.

2 Dispersion

INTRODUCTION

1 This Chapter considers the spread of data about the maen. Just as there are different measures of central tendency so there are different measures of spread. We consider four measures of spread about the mean. They are;

> **The Range**
> **The Mean Absolute Deviation**
> **The Variance**
> **Standard Deviation**

There are five major parts to this Chapter. They are;

> **Dispersion**
> **Measures of Dispersion**
> **Comparing Statistics**
> **Coefficient Of Variation**
> **Grouped Data**

DISPERSION

2 Dispersion is concerned with how the data is dispersed or spread over the whole range of values of the data. Whilst the single statistics of mean, mode and median give an indication of the central tendency of the data the single statistics of dispersion give an indication of how the data is spread.

MEASURES OF DISPERSION

3 It is possible to measure the spread of data about any datum. What is of general interest is the spread of data about a centre. The particular centre that we shall consider here is the mean and the four measures of spread are;

> **Range**
> **Mean Absolute Deviation**
> **Variance**
> **Standard Deviation**

RANGE

4 The range of the data is the difference between the highest datum value and the lowest. For example, the data

$$25, 90, 33, 12, 48$$

has 90 as its highest value and 12 as its lowest so the range is

$$90 - 12 = 78.$$

Whilst the range does not tell us HOW the data is distributed it does tell us the EXTENT of the spread.

MEAN ABSOLUTE DEVIATION

5 Perhaps the simplest single measure of spread is that which measures the average deviation from the mean. Consider the five numbers

$$1, 2, 3, 4, 5$$

The arithmetic mean of these numbers is 3. Only one of these numbers is equal to the mean, the other four are different. We now construct a table which contains the differences between these five numbers and the mean. These differences are called DEVIATIONS FROM THE MEAN.

Number	Deviation from the mean
1	3 - 1 = 2
2	3 - 2 = 1
3	3 - 3 = 0
4	3 - 4 = -1
5	3 - 5 = -2

If we add up these deviations we obtain zero. The total of all the deviations from the mean is ZERO! This means, of course, that the AVERAGE DEVIATION FROM THE MEAN is zero. The reason for this result lies in the negative deviations. The sum of the deviations of the numbers less than the mean equals minus the sum of the deviations of those numbers greater than the mean. The net effect is that the deviations cancel each other out. This is only to be expected because the mean is a centre point of the data. As far as dispersion is concerned we are not interested in the DIRECTION of the deviation. What we require is the MAGNITUDE of the deviation. Accordingly we ignore signs. We do this by taking what is called the ABSOLUTE VALUES of the deviations from the mean. The absolute value of a negative number is the number without its minus sign. The absolute value of a positive number is the number itself. We construct a new table, this time including the absoluted deviations.

Number	Deviation from mean	Absolute Deviation
1	3 - 1 = 2	2
2	3 - 2 = 1	1
3	3 - 3 = 0	0
4	3 - 4 = -1	1
5	3 - 5 = -2	2
		TOTAL 6

The sum of the absolute deviations is 6. The **total absolute deviation from the mean is 6.** If we now divide this number by 5 we obtain the AVERAGE ABSOLUTED DEVIATION FROM THE MEAN - namely

$$6 \div 5 = 1.2$$

The MEAN ABSOLUTE DEVIATION (MAD for short) from the mean is 1.2. The Mean absolute deviation is sometimes referred to as the MEAN DEVIATION.

THE VARIANCE

6 We have just seen that allowing negative deviations from the mean results in a total deviation of ZERO. Instead of overcoming this by stripping the sign off the negative deviations we can SQUARE the deviations. This has the effect of converting all negative deviations into positive squared deviations because when two negative numbers are multiplied together the result is a positive number. Consider the following table,

Number	Deviation from the mean	Squared Deviation
1	3 - 1 = 2	4
2	3 - 2 = 1	1
3	3 - 3 = 0	0
4	3 - 4 = -1	1
5	3 - 5 = -2	4
		TOTAL 10

The total squared deviation is thus 10 which produces an AVERAGE SQUARED DEVIATION of

$$10 \div 5 = 2$$

This quantity is called the VARIANCE.

STANDARD DEVIATION

7 The STANDARD DEVIATION is the square root of the variance. Since the variance was obtained by adding squares of differences, taking the square root of that sum is a natural thing to do. The standard deviation is the most commonly used measure of dispersion and is fundamental to Statistics. We found in the last paragraph that the variance for the data was 2. Consequently, the standard deviation is;

$$\sqrt{2} = 1.414.....$$

152

COMPARING STATISTICS

8 Producing the mean and the dispersion of a collection of data is all very well but their significance is not really appreciated until comparisons are made with another collection of data.

Two friends were comparing their examination marks at the end of the year. Joe and Bill's marks are tabulated below;

Subject	Joe	Bill
MATHEMATICS	68	72
GEOGRAPHY	54	83
HISTORY	57	76
ART	70	40
BIOLOGY	91	45
CHEMISTRY	83	67
ENGLISH	65	71
FRENCH	48	82
TOTAL	536	536
AVERAGE	67	67

We see that both Joe and Bill obtained the same average. But how did they perform with regard to consistency? To find this out we measure the standard deviation of each set of marks. This is done in the following table. Notice how the table is constructed. Joe and Bill's marks and the calculations made on them are listed side by side. At the bottom of the table the same pattern is followed. Recording the marks and calculations in this way allow the comparison between the two sets of results to be read more easily. Also, including the calculations allows them to be quickly checked for accuracy.

JOE			BILL		
Number	Mean – Number	Square	Number	Mean – Number	Square
68	67 – 68 = -1	1	72	67 – 72 = -5	25
54	67 – 54 = 13	169	83	67 – 83 = -16	256
57	67 – 57 = 10	100	76	67 – 76 = -9	81
70	67 – 70 = -3	9	40	67 – 40 = 27	729
91	67 – 91 = -24	576	45	67 – 45 = 22	484
83	67 – 83 = -16	256	67	67 – 67 = 0	0
65	67 – 65 = 2	4	71	67 – 71 = -4	16
48	67 – 48 = 19	361	82	67 – 82 = -15	225

TOTAL 1476	TOTAL 1816
VARIANCE = 1476 ÷ 8 = 184.5	VARIANCE = 1816 ÷ 8 = 227
STANDARD DEVIATION = 13.6	STANDARD DEVIATION = 15.1

Clearly Joe's marks were closest to the average as he had the smaller standard deviation. It could be argued that Joe was more consistent in his examinations than Bill. In this example Joe and Bill had the same average mark. It then makes sense to look at their respective standard deviations to distinguish one set of marks from the other. If their averages had been different as well as their standard deviations then a comparison would have been more difficult. For example, suppose Tom had an average mark of 58 with a standard deviation of 1 and Jack had an average mark of 60 with a standard deviation of 1.5. Comparing these two sets of statistics becomes confusing. Whilst Tom had the lower average his marks were more consistent than Jack's. So which student has the better results overall? To answer this question a further statistic is introduced, the Coefficient of Variation.

COEFFICIENT OF VARIATION

9 The COEFFICIENT OF VARIATION is defined as **the amount of standard deviation per unit of the mean.** Symbolically it is given as;

$$[(\text{standard deviation}) \div (\text{mean})] \times 100$$

The coefficient of variation will allow two different sets of data each with different means and different standard deviations to be sensibly compared. In the same set of examinations Tom and Jack obtained both different means and different standard deviations. These are recorded in the following table.

EXAMINATION STATISTICS	Tom	Jack
Mean Mark	58	1.0
Standard Deviation	60	1.5

Using the statistics in this table the Coefficients of Variation are calculated for Tom and Jack.

$$\text{Tom's Coefficient of Variation} = (1 \div 58) \times 100$$
$$= 1.7$$

$$\text{Jack's Coefficient of Variation} = (1.5 \div 60) \times 100$$
$$= 2.5$$

In this case, despite Tom having the lower average mark, he has the lower coefficient of variation and is, therefore, the more consistent student.

GROUPED DATA

10 In this last paragraph we demonstrate how a similar calculation can be performed on grouped data - that is data where each datum occurs with a given frequency. The following table records the withdrawals from an automatic teller during some period of time.

AMOUNT (£)	FREQUENCY	TOTAL (£)
10	12	120
20	82	1640
30	125	3750
40	74	2960
50	7	350
TOTAL	**300**	**8820**

That is a total of 300 withdrawals withdrew a total of £8820. The average withdrawal, therefore, was

$$\text{£8820} \div 300 = \text{£29.40}$$

We now come to the calculation of the standard deviation and for this we construct the following table;

Amount	Mean – Amount	$(\text{Difference})^2$	Frequency	TOTAL
10	29.40−10=19.4	376.36	12	4516.32
20	29.40−20= 9.4	88.36	82	7245.52
30	29.40−30=−.60	.36	125	45.00
40	29.40−40=−10.6	112.36	74	8314.64
50	29.40−50=−20.6	424.36	7	2970.52
			TOTAL	**23092.00**
VARIANCE = 23092 ÷ 300 = 76.97				
STANDARD DEVIATION = 8.8				

Notice that in the totals column each number is obtained by multiplying the corresponding squared difference from the mean by its frequency.

SUMMARY

11 Any collection of data has a measure of central tendency and a measure of spread about that centre. There are four measures of spread that we have considered here. The range measures the total spread of the data between its extreme values. The mean absolute deviation measures the average deviation magnitude from the mean. The variance measures the average squared deviation from the mean. The Standard Deviation is the square root of the variance and is the most commonly used single dispersion statistic. For comparing two sets of data with different means and different standard deviations the Coefficient of Variation is used.

KEY POINTS TO NOTE

12 Dispersion, Range, Mean absolute deviation, Variance, Standard deviation, Coefficient of variance, Comparing statistics.

STUDENT SELF TESTING

SELF REVIEW QUESTIONS

1. What is dispersion concerned with? (2)

2. List four single statistics of dispersion. (3)

3. What is the range? (4)

4. What is the absolute value of a number? (5)

5. What is the Mean Absolute Deviation? (5)

6. What is the variance? (6)

7. What is the purpose of squaring numbers to compute the variance? (7)

8. What is the standard deviation? (8)

9. What is the coefficient of variation? (9)

EXERCISES (Answers begin on Page 249)

1 a) What is the meaning of the term *Measure of Dispersion* ?

b) What is the range of a set of data? Give one advantage and one disadvantage of the range as a measure of dispersion.

c) The sales (in £) of each branch of a chain of stores was recorded for a particular day. The results were

$$464, 521, 386, 479, 545, 361, 418, 492, 503, 431$$

Calculate the mean deviation and the standard deviation of the sales.

LCCI 1985

2 The duration of each telephone call made by an employee was recorded for a period of one week. The results are shown in the following table.

Duration (minutes)	Number of calls
under 3	45
3 and under 6	59
6 and under 9	38
9 and under 12	31
12 and under 15	19
15 and under 18	8
18 and over	0

a) Calculate the mean and standard deviation of the duration of these calls.

b) Use these values to calculate the coefficient of variation.

LCCI 1984

3. a) What is meant by a measure of dispersion?

b) Name and calculate three measures of dispersion using the folloeing raw data.

Lengths of Journeys made by Sales Representatives of X Co.
(data in kilometers)

263, 227, 234, 258, 233, 216, 245, 239, 227, 241, 242, 213, 204, 227, 263, 250, 214, 226, 232, 246.

LCCI 1983

4. The following grouped frequency table gives information concerning the delay in payments of amounts outstanding.

No. of days delay in payment	No. of accounts
1 to 6	21
7 to 13	46
14 to 20	73
21 to 27	27
28 to 34	24
35 to 41	9

Calculate the standard deviation of delay in payment correct to three significant figures. If the mean delay in payment is 18 days, what is the coefficient of variation?

LCC! 1982

5. The heights of 12 people are recorded below.

Height in centimeters

181, 174, 169, 163, 179, 176
179, 175, 167, 176, 168, 187

Calculate
- a) the range
- b) the mean absolute deviation
- c) the variance
- d) the standard deviation
- e) the coefficient of variation

6. The population in a certain area of the country is listed in the following table.

Age Group	Males (000's)	Females (000's)
0 - 20	251	241
21 - 40	209	215
41 - 60	128	128
61 - 80	84	95
81+	16	24

By calculating the coefficient of variation for males amd females find out whether female ages vary more than male ages.

3 Multiple Statistics

INTRODUCTION

1 This Chapter deals with the need to extract more information from data than can be provided by the single statistics discussed in Chapters 1 and 2 of this Section. This further information is obtained by using FRACTILES. The fractiles considered are QUARTILES, DECILES and PERCENTILES. Finally a further single statistic of dispersion is derived, the QUARTILE DEVIATION.

There are three major parts to this Chapter. They are;

> **Multiple Statistics**
> **Fractiles**
> **Graphical Determination Of Fractiles**

MULTIPLE STATISTICS

2 We saw in the last two chapters that reducing data to statistics is the means whereby we summarize the information contained in the data. If, however, we reduce to too few statistics then a certain amount of information can be lost. We saw this with dispersion. By describing the spread of the data with a single statistic such as the variance or standard deviation then the information obtained is only of real use when comparing one set of data with another. In order to retain more information about the spread of a single set of data we now learn how to derive a collection of statistics associated with a single set of data. These MULTIPLE STATISTICS are called FRACTILES.

FRACTILES

3 A FRACTILE is a statistic that denotes the boundary of a FRACTIONAL PART OF THE DATA. The simplest fractile is the MEDIAN. The median denotes the boundary between two equal halves of the data. We can say that half of the data have values less than the median and the other half have values greater than the median. The median is, however, a single statistic and here we are to consider multiple statistics. The most commonly used multiple fractiles are

> **Quartiles**
> **Deciles**
> **Percentiles**

QUARTILES

4 There are three quartiles and they divide the data into FOUR EQUAL PARTS. The LOWER QUARTILE is ONE QUARTER the way through the data arranged in ascending order. The UPPER QUARTILE is THREE QUARTERS the way through the data. The MIDDLE QUARTILE is TWO QUARTERS, that is HALFWAY through the data and is of course identical to the Median. The quartiles can be calculated in the same way as the median. For example, the numbers

> **2, 4, 6, 8, 10, 12, 14**

are split as follows.

Q_1 the lower quartile

5 The position of the lower quartile is obtained by ADDING 1 TO THE NUMBER OF DATA ITEMS AND DIVIDING BY 4. Thus the position of the lower quartile is equal to

$$(7+1) \div 4 \; = \; 2$$

It is the second number in the sequence. This means that 4 is the lower quartile.

Q_3 the upper quartile

6 The position of the upper quartile is obtained in a similar manner except that being three-quarters the way through the data we multiply the lower quartile position by 3. Thus the position of the upper quartile is equal to

$$3 \times (7+1) \div 4 \; = \; 6$$

It is the sixth number in the sequence. This means that 12 is the upper quartile.

M the median

7 The position of the Median then follows as being equal to

$$2 \times (7+1) \div 4 \; = \; 4$$

It is the fourth number in the sequence. This means that 8 is the median

From a knowledge of the quartiles we obtain a clearer picture of how the data is spread through its range.

EXAMPLE

The ages of the employees of a company are given in the following table;

Age	Number
15 and under 25	30
25 and under 35	76
35 and under 45	38
45 and under 55	10
55 and under 65	5
TOTAL	159

Find the upper and lower quartiles and comment briefly on the result.

There are a total of 159 employees and if they were ranked according to age the position of the lower quartile in the ranking would be

$$(159+1) \div 4 = 40$$

From this fact we can obtain the lower quartile age Q_1. Since the first 30 in the ranking would be aged under 25 years the 40th ranked age must lie between 25 years and 35 years. This interval of 10 years contains 76 employees so the average age difference between any two adjacently ranked employees must be

$$10 \div 76 \text{ years}$$

We are looking for the 10th employee in that ranking so that employee's age must be 10 intervals along the ranking. This means that the lower quartile age is

$$Q_1 = 25 + (10 \div 76)\text{x}10$$

$$= 25 + 1.3$$

$$= 26.3 \text{ years}$$

By a similar reasoning the position in the ranking of the upper quartile age is

$$3\text{x}(159+1) \div 4 = 120$$

This position lies within the 34 -45 age range. It is in fact the 14th along the ranking. This means that the upper quartile age Q_3 is

$$Q_3 = 35 + (10 \div 38) \text{ x } 14$$

$$= 35 + 3.7$$

$$= 38.7 \text{ years}$$

From these results we can conclude that the lowest quarter of employees are aged between 15 and 26.3 years. The upper quarter of employees are aged between 38.7 and 65 years. Half of the employees are aged between 26.3 and 38.7 years. So there is a high concentration of employees aged between 25 and 40.

QUARTILE DEVIATION

8 A further single statistic of dispersion can now be introduced. It is the QUARTILE DEVIATION. This is defined as;

$$(Q_3 - Q_1) \div 2$$

In the previous example concerning employees ages the quartile deviation is

$$(38.7 - 26.3) \div 2 = 6.2$$

Considering that the range of ages is 50 years this small quartile deviation bears out the earlier conclusion that there is a high concentration of employees in the middle years.

DECILES

9 There are 9 DECILES and they divide the data into 10 equal parts. The positon of the deciles are calculated in just the same manner as the Quartiles except we divide by 10 instead of 4. For example, in a list of 99 data items the position of the 6th decile is equal to

$$6 \times (99 + 1) \div 10 = 60$$

The 60th datum in then the 6th decile.

Reverting to the earlier example of employees ages we find that, for example, the position in the ranking of the fourth decile D_4 is equal to

$$4 \times (159+1) \div 10 = 64$$

This lies in the 25 - 35 year interval and is the 34th ranked age in that inerval. This means that the 4th decile age is D_4 is

$$D_4 = 25 + (10 \div 76) \times 34$$

$$= 25 + 4.5$$

$$= 29.4 \text{ years}$$

PERCENTILES

10 There are 99 PERCENTILES and they divide the data into 100 equal parts. Again, the position of any particular percentile is obtained in a similar manner to otaining the positions of quartiles and deciles. For example, the position of the 35th percentile is

$$35 \times (N + 1) \div 100$$

where N is the number of data items.

From our earlier example concerning employees ages we find that, for example, the position in the ranking of the 80th percentile P_{80} is equal to

$$80 \times (159+1) \div 100 = 128$$

This lies in the 35 - 45 year interval and is the 22nd ranked age in that inerval, there being a total of 106 employees ranked in the first two intervals. This means that the 80th percentile age is P_{80} is

$$P_{80} = 35 + (10 \div 38) \times 22$$
$$= 35 + 5.8$$
$$= 40.8 \text{ years}$$

GRAPHICAL DETERMINATION OF FRACTILES

11 We can obtain fractiles graphically in the same way that we obtained the median in Chapter 1 of this Section. For example, from the frequency table that contains the ages of the 159 employees of a certain company we can construct the following cumulative frequency table.

Age	Number	Cumulative Frequency
15 and under 25	30	30
25 and under 35	76	106
35 and under 45	38	144
45 and under 55	10	154
55 and under 65	5	159
TOTAL	**159**	

From the cumulative frequency values in this table the cumulative frequency graph can be plotted. Notice that the numbers of employees (cumulative frequencies) in a given age interval are plotted at the highest end point of that interval.

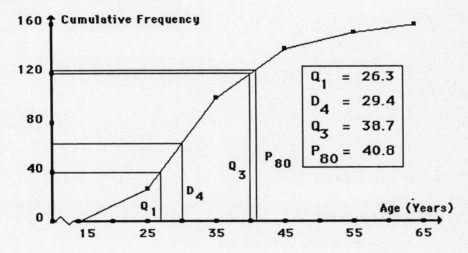

Treating this cumulative frequency graph in the same way that we treated the similar graph in Chapter 6 of Section 3 the various fractiles can be read off as shown. The values so found are listed in the box.

SUMMARY

12 Recognising the limitations of single statistics of dispersion further information can be obtained from data by looking at its spread over regular intervals of the range. The quartiles and median describe the spread over four quarters of the range. Similary the deciles and percentiles describe the spread over tenths and hundredths of the range respectively. By considering such fractiles a more detailed description of the spread of the data can be made.

KEY POINTS TO NOTE

13 Fractiles, Quartiles, Quartile deviaton, Deciles, Percentiles

STUDENT SELF TESTING

SELF REVIEW QUESTIONS

1. Why are multiple statistics required? (2)

2. What are fractiles? (3)

3. What is a quartile? (4)

4. What is the quartile deviation? (8)

5. What is a decile? (9)

6. What is a percentile? (10)

7. How do we calculate fractiles for grouped data? (7,9,10,)

8. What do we need to calculate the fractiles graphically? (11)

EXERCISES (Answers begin on Page 249)

1. From the graph estimate the median, the upper quartile, the lower quartile, the 10th percentile and the 90th percentile

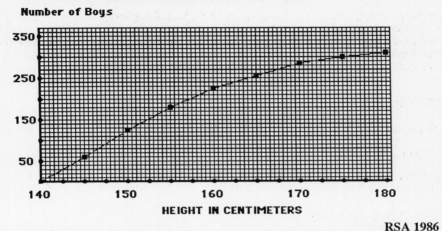

Cumulative Frequency graph of heights of 320 schoolboys

RSA 1986

2 A biologist measured the lengths of 100 cuckoo eggs which he found in nests. He illustrated the results by the cumulative frequency diagram shown below.

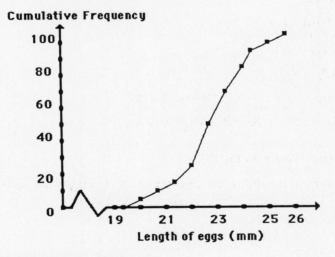

a) What was the *range* of his measurements?

b) Read as accurately as you can the median and the quartiles of length and explain what these tell you.

c) Someone asked him what sort of size most cuckoo eggs are. What answer might he have given?

d) Why do you think he 'broke' the horizontal (length) axis between 0 and 19?

e) If you find an egg, which you think is a cuckoo egg, and it measures 18.5 mm in length, how confident can you be that is *is* a cuckoo egg?

RSA 1984

3. The number of customers who bought petrol in multiple units of £1 were counted and recorded in the following table.

£	Number
1	1
2	5
3	10
4	15
5	30
6	14

Construct a cumulative frequency graph and find;

a) the median

b) the upper and lower quartiles

c) the quartile deviation

4. In an examination sat by 60 students the following marks were recorded as percentages.

8	15	65	41	85	55	64	46	74	79
72	58	62	25	67	18	83	53	38	69
45	75	5	63	91	57	42	92	53	48
33	51	31	47	74	71	4	66	58	76
65	55	19	87	41	64	32	25	28	81
74	52	83	60	89	0	16	43	66	18

a) Construct a cumulative frequency graph in intervals of ten marks

b) Find the 10th and 90th percentiles.

c) How many students lie between the 25th and 75th percentiles?

5 Using the data from Question 5 show that

$$P_{25} = Q_1$$

$$P_{75} = Q_3$$

Do you think that this result will be true for any set of data? Explain your reasoning.

6 The number of faults in 40 new washing machines are listed in the following table.

$$
\begin{array}{cccccccccc}
0 & 4 & 1 & 2 & 0 & 5 & 1 & 0 & 2 & 4 \\
5 & 0 & 5 & 0 & 4 & 3 & 3 & 0 & 4 & 5 \\
0 & 4 & 3 & 4 & 3 & 0 & 4 & 2 & 0 & 3 \\
1 & 0 & 2 & 0 & 5 & 4 & 1 & 1 & 4 & 0 \\
\end{array}
$$

a) Plot a cumulative frequency graph and obtain the 4th and 8th deciles.

b) Rank the data in ascending order and find the 4th and 8th deciles by calculation. Compare your results with the results found in a)

4 Index Numbers

INTRODUCTION

1 This Chapter deals with Index Numbers. Starting from the single price relative the weighted aggregative index is developed. Both Laspeyre and Paasche indexes are covered. The creation of an index and its manipulation are also considered. The Chapter concludes with a description of the General Retail Prices Index.

There are nine major parts to this Chapter. They are;

> **Index Numbers**
> **Prices Relative**
> **Weighted Aggregative Indexes**
> **Laspeyre Index**
> **Paasche Index**
> **Chain Base Index**
> **Change of Base Year**
> **Creation Of An Index**
> **The Retail Prices Index.**

INDEX NUMBERS

2 An INDEX NUMBER is a statistic that shows the average change in a quantity over a period of time. For example, if the average house price in a given region of the country for three successive years is given in the following table as;

YEAR	PRICE
1985	£20,000
1986	£28,000
1987	£34,000

By dividing the 1986 price by the 1985 price we obtain

$$28,000 \div 20,000 = 1.4$$

That is, the 1986 price is 0.4 times greater than the 1985 price. These proportions are best expressed as percentages so we multiply by 100. That is

$$(28,000 \div 20,000) \times 100 = 140$$

The 1986 price is 40% greater than the 1985 price. Repeating this for the following year;

$$(34,000 \div 20,000) \times 100 = 170$$

The 1987 price is 70% greater than the 1985 price. These percentages are called INDEX NUMBERS. Let us complete the table as follows;

YEAR	PRICE	INDEX
1985	£20,000	100
1986	£28,000	140
1987	£34,000	170

3 Notice that the first index is 100. That is

$$(20,000 \div 20,000) \times 100 = 100$$

The year 1985 is called the BASE YEAR. It is the year upon which the subsequent indexes are BASED. By looking at the indexes we have a more absolute impression of how the price of houses has changed over the three years. Also, using these percentages we can compute the expected price change of a particular house. For example, a house worth £30,000 in 1985 should be worth

$$£30,000 \times 1.7 = £51,000 \text{ in } 1987$$

PRICE RELATIVE

4 When the price change of a single commodity is experessed by means of an index number then the index is referred to as a PRICE RELATIVE. What is of more interest is the WEIGHTED AGGREGATIVE INDEX of a number of commodities.

WEIGHTED AGGREGATIVE INDEX

5 Many times it is desired to reduce the price change of a number of different items to a single index number. Such is the case with the RETAIL PRICES INDEX where a number of commodities are reduced to a single index number. We shall look at the Retail Price Index at the end of this Chapter.

The problem of reducing a number of different items to a single index lies in the relative merits of each item. Let us consider the case of just two items, milk and motor oil. Ordinarily, an individual could buy a quantity of milk every day and a quantity of motor oil hardly ever at all. As a result, if we were considering our budget then a rise in the price of milk would be immediately felt but a rise in the price of motor oil would not be of such immediate importance. We shall take a litre of milk to cost 40p and a litre of motor oil to cost £1.00 in our base year of 1984. The increase in these two prices for the next four years is recorded in the following table;

YEAR	MILK	MOTOR OIL
1984	40	100
1985	42	108
1986	44	112
1987	50	122

We shall further assume milk to be more important to us than motor oil in the ratio 10 to 1. In other words we buy 10 times more milk than motor oil. We now multiply the prices by these WEIGHTS of 10 and 1 respectively and so construct our weighted aggregative index.

YEAR	MILK	WEIGHTED x(10)	OIL	WEIGHTED x(1)	SUM	INDEX
1984	0.40	4.00	1.00	1.00	5.00	100
1985	0.42	4.20	1.08	1.08	5.28	106 = (5.28÷5.00)x100
1986	0.44	4.40	1.12	1.12	5.52	110 = (5.52÷5.00)x100
1987	0.50	5.50	1.22	1.22	6.22	124 = (6.22÷5.00)x100

6 The essence of the WEIGHTED AGGREGATIVE INDEX is that it reflects the price changes with respect to a particular purchasing pattern. The purchasing pattern is taken account of by means of the WEIGHTS. Just to show how the resultant index depends upon the relative weightings given to the individual items let us repeat this exercise. This time we shall consider the case of a motor mechanic who buys 10 times more motor oil than milk. The corresponding calculations follow.

YEAR	MILK	WEIGHTED x(1)	OIL	WEIGHTED x(10)	SUM	INDEX
1984	0.40	0.40	1.00	10.00	10.40	100
1985	0.42	0.42	1.08	10.80	11.22	108 = (11.22÷10.40)x100
1986	0.44	0.44	1.12	11.20	11.64	112 = (11.64÷10.40)x100
1987	0.50	0.50	1.22	12.20	12.70	122 = (12.70÷10.40)x100

As we see the index numbers are different from the original ones. To the person buying more milk than motor oil the index increased by 6, 4 and 14 points in successive years. To the motor mechanic the index increased by 8, 4 and 10 points during the same successive years. This raises a veru important point about indexes. **We must always be aware of the reason for calculating them and to whom or to what purchasing pattern they apply.**

LASPEYRE INDEX

7 The Laspeyre Index compares the cost of buying base year quantities at current year prices with the cost of buying base year quantities at base year prices. In other words, if we bought a shopping basket of goods LAST YEAR the Laspeyre Index will compare its cost now with its cost last year.

The following table records the quantities purchsed of X, Y and Z against the prices paid for them last year and this year.

Item	Quantity Last Year	Price Last Year	Price This Year
X	100	25p	45p
Y	50	120p	200p
Z	30	40p	65p

We use the quantities as weights since that is the best way to reflect their relative importance. The following table shows how the Laspeyre Index is evaluated. Q denotes the quantity. P1 and P2 denote the prices per unit last year and this year respectively.

ITEM	Q	P1	QxP1	P2	QxP2
X	100	25	2500	45	4500
Y	50	120	6000	200	10000
Z	30	40	1200	65	1950
TOTALS			9700		16450

Laspeyre Index = (16450 ÷ 9700) x 100

= 170

PAASCHE INDEX

8 The Paasche Index compares the cost of buying current year quantities at current year prices with the cost of buying current year quantities at base year prices. In other words, if we bought a shopping basket of goods THIS year the Paasche Index will compare its cost now with the cost it would have been last year. We shall use the same data as before to construct the Paasche Index for our items X, Y and Z with this year's quantites used instead of last year's..

Item	Quantity This Year	Price Last Year	Price This Year
X	120	25p	45p
Y	40	120p	200p
Z	50	40p	65p

Again we use the quantities as weights since that is the best way to reflect their relative importance. The following table shows how the Paasche Index is evaluated.

ITEM	Q	P1	QxP1	P2	QxP2
X	120	25	3000	45	5400
Y	40	120	4800	200	8000
Z	50	40	2000	65	3250
TOTALS			9800		16650

Paasche Index = (16650 ÷ 9800) x 100

= 173

LASPEYRE AND PAASCHE CONTRASTED

9 The Paasche Index requires the quantities to be measured each year and this can be a costly exercise. Also, since the denominator in the index changes each year we can only compare one year's Paasche Index with the base year. The Paasche Index does, however, keep abreast of current purchasing patterns as it continually updates the items in the shopping basket.

In contrast the Laspeyre index only requires a record of current prices. Also, since the denominator in the index remains the same then each year's index can be compared with any other year's index. This makes the Laspeyre index the more popular of the two despite the fact that this index does not take into account any change in the purchasing pattern. The contents of the shopping basket remain the same as the base year.

CHAIN BASE INDEX

10 With a chain base index the base year progresses a year at a time so that each index is measured relative to the previous year. The following example illustrates this. The table records the weekending price of a share quoted on the London Stock exchange over a period of 7 weeks.

PRICE	INDEX
28p	100
32p	$(32\div28)\times100 = 114$
34p	$(34\div32)\times100 = 106$
45p	$(45\div34)\times100 = 132$
54p	$(54\div45)\times100 = 120$
63p	$(63\div54)\times100 = 117$
84 p	$(84\div63)\times100 = 102$

The chain base index shows how the rate of change is changing as well as the extent of the change over the previous year. For example, over the second week the share price increased by

$$132 - 106 = 26\%.$$

Over the sixth week the share price decreased by **12%**.

CHANGE OF BASE YEAR

11 An index is obtained by dividing by a base year price. If each index number is then multiplied by the old base year price and then divided by the new base year price a new index will have been formed against a new base year. For example, the following table records five successive prices and their indexes calculated first with year 1 as base year and secondly with year 3 as base year.

	Price	Index Based on Year 1	Index Based on Year 2
Year 1	20	$(20\div20)\times100 = 100$	$(100\times20)\div40 = 50$
Year 2	30	$(30\div20)\times100 = 150$	$(150\times20)\div40 = 75$
Year 3	40	$(40\div20)\times100 = 200$	$(200\times20)\div40 = 100$
Year 4	50	$(50\div20)\times100 = 250$	$(250\times20)\div40 = 125$
Year 5	60	$(60\div20)\times100 = 300$	$(300\times20)\div40 = 150$

Notice that the new index has been taken back to a time before the new base year, in which case the index is less than 100.

THE CREATION OF AN INDEX

12 When creating an index we must consider the following points;

The purpose for which it will be used
The choice of base year

THE PURPOSE FOR WHICH IT WILL BE USED

13 An index is constructed using a collection of specific commodities. The price of each commodity is multiplied by a specific weight that rates its relative importance within the collection. For these reasons the index should only be used where both the chosen commodities and their associated weights are appropriate. For example, we saw earlier that an index constructed from the prices of milk and motor oil would change for different choices of relative weights. For a motor mechanic it would be more appropriate to heavily weight the motor oil. for anyone else the milk would carry the heavier weighting. As a result an index appropriate to a motor mechanic would be an inappropriate index for anyone else and vice versa. Because of this the people who are going to use the index must be borne in mind. Having identified the people then the appropriate commodities aand associated weights must be used.

CHOICE OF BASE YEAR

14 The last point to consider is when to start the index. The base year should be a *normal* year when no abnormal changes have occurred. If a year of abnormal change is chosen as a the base year then further years of minor change will hardly show at all. This will give misleading conclusions of the true situation. Finally, the base year must not be chosen to be too far in the past. Too early a base year could make current changes irrelevant in comparison.

THE RETAIL PRICES INDEX

15 The General Index of Retail Prices otherwise known as the Retail Prices Index measures the change in the cost of living. The index is complied for the Government and published each month in the Monthly Digest of Statistics. Since it measures the monthly change in the cost of living it is widely used as a measure of inflation.

The index is constructed from the prices of what is called a **representative basket of goods**. This basket of goods contains items that are bought each month by a typical household. The items and the quantities bought each month are listed in the Family Expenditure Survey. The Family Expenditure Survey is a continuing enquiry conducted by the Department of Employment. It investigates the general characteristics of households, their incomes and their expenditures. From this information the representative basket of goods is divided into the following groups;

Food and Catering
Alcohol and Tobacco
Housing and Housing Expenditure
Personal Expenditure
Travel and Leisure

FOOD AND CATERING

16 The food referred to consists of various staples such as bread, dairy produce, meats and vegetables. The catering refers to meals bought in restaurants, canteens and take-away outlets. This section covers 22% of the basket of goods.

ALCOHOL AND TOBACCO

17 This group covers beers, wines and spirits and all tobacco products. It accounts for 11% of the basket of goods.

HOUSING AND HOUSEHOLD EXPENDITURE

18 Housing refers to such items as rents, mortgages, rates and other costs typical of maintaining a house. The household expenditure refers to household consumables, appliances and furniture. This section accounts for 32% of the basket of goods.

PERSONAL EXPENDITURE

19 Personal expenditure covers clothing and personal services. This accounts for 11% of the basket of goods.

TRAVEL AND LEISURE

20 This group consists of holiday costs, entertainment, sports goods, car costs, petrol and a number of other items. It accounts for 13% of the basket of goods.

21 In the representative basket of goods there are 1000 items and each item has associated with it an index or price relative. Also associated with each item is a weight that rates the relative importance of that item in the basket of goods. Each item index is multiplied by its weight to produce a single WEIGHTED INDEX. All these weighted indexes are then added and the result divided by 1000. This yields the **Retail Prices Index**. Consequently, the Retail Prices Index is an average of weighted price relatives. The base month of the index is January 1987 following various revisions in items and weights. Before the revision the base month was January 1974 and by January 1987 the index stood at nearly 400.

22 The Retail Prices Index has been criticised for not being truly representative of all households. For example, a single poor pensioner will not buy the same basket of goods as a high income earner. Not only would the items differ but so would their relative importance. In recognition of this each of these two groups have their own index separate from the General Index of Retail Prices. Furthermore, the items and their weights in the basket of goods are continually revised to ensure that it remains as representative as possible.

SUMMARY

23 An index number shows the average change in the price of a number of commodities over a period of time. A weighted aggregative index shows the average change in the price of a number of commodities - the price of each commodity weighted according to its relative importance. The index is measured against a fixed year called the base year. In the base year the index has a value of 100. Two notable indexes are the Laspeyre Index and the Paasche Index. The Laspeyre Index compares the cost of buying base year quantities at current year prices with the cost of buying base year quantities at base year prices. The Paasche Index compares the cost of buying current year quantities at current year prices with the cost of buying current year quantities at base year prices. It is possible to construct an index that each year measures a comparison with the previous year. This is the chain base index. It is also possible to change the base year. When constructing an index it is important to know who the index is for. This will then determine the commodities to be included and what weightings are appropriate. Also the choice of base year is important. Chosing a year during which abnormal changes occured will cause subsequent moderate annual changes to be underestimated. Perhaps the most well known index is the Retail Price Index which is used as a measure of inflation.

KEY POINTS TO NOTE

24 Index numbers, Price relative, Weighted aggregative index, Base year, Laspeyre index, Paasche index, Chain base index, Change of base, Retail Price Index.

STUDENT SELF TESTING

SELF REVIEW QUESTIONS

1. What is an index number? (2)

2. What is the Base Year? (3)

3. What is a price relative? (4)

4. What is a weighted aggregative index? (5,6)

5. What does the Laspeyre Index compare? (7)

6. What does the Paasche Index compare? (8)

7. What is a Chain Base Index? (10)

8. List two important factors to be considered when creating an index. (12-14)

9. What is the Retail Prices Index? (15, 21)

10. List the six categories in the Retail Prices Index. (15-20)

EXERCISES (Answers begin on Page 249)

1. Explain the difference between base weighting and current weighting for the calculation of index numbers. State some advantages and disadvantages of each.

LCCI 1985

2. The following table shows the agricultural output of Great Britain, in millions of £ at 1975 prices.

Year	Wheat	Barley	Potatoes	Beet	Other	TOTAL
1971	224	263	348	144		1053
1973	274	335	353	128		1170
1976	246	302	230	88		940
1978	292	402	328	132		1242
1981	430	410	367	133		1456

(Source: Annual Abstract of Statistics, 1983)

a) Complete this table

b) Using 1971 as the base year, construct a series of index numbers for each commodity for each year.

RSA 1985

3. Describe the construction of an index to measure the change in retail prices.

LCCI 1984

4.   **Consumption in the home of selected foods**

Great Britain	Indexes of average quantities per person per week. 1975 = 100						
	1961	**1966**	**1971**	**1975**	**1977**	**1979**	**1981**
Type of Food							
Liquid milk	103	104	100	100	95	91	84
Cheese	81	82	96	100	100	101	103
Eggs	113	115	110	100	97	94	89
Beef and Veal	109	98	96	100	99	99	84
Mutton and Lamb	159	148	127	100	93	101	100
Pork	71	101	111	100	122	133	140
Poultry, uncooked	42	70	85	100	107	118	127
All other meat and meat prod	101	105	109	100	105	108	106
Fish and fish products	128	130	115	100	93	101	110
Butter	110	108	98	100	83	79	66
Margerine	127	107	121	100	134	140	158
All other fats	88	94	100	100	97	102	112
Fresh potatoes	129	120	112	100	93	99	95
Othe fresh vegetables[1]	113	108	110	100	106	104	109
Othe fresh vegetables and vegetable products[2]	67	78	86	100	99	109	116
Fresh fruit	99	109	115	100	100	112	114
Othe fruit and fruit products	99	102	104	100	94	99	123
Bread	134	113	106	100	97	93	93
Cakes, biscuits etc.	119	123	115	100	96	97	93
Sugar	160	151	140	100	107	102	98
Tea	130	121	110	100	95	97	91
Instant Coffee	32	58	88	100	72	102	104

[1] Irrespective of age
[2] Includes tomatoes

Source: National Food Survey. Ministry of Agriculture, Fisheries and Food

a) Explain the remark '1975 = 100' in the heading

b) For fresh tomatoes, using the year 1961 as 100, calculate the index for 1981

c) On the same graph plot the indexes for beef and veal and for pork, over the whole period shown in the table

d) For instant coffee, construct a chain base index showing the variations from 1961 to 1966, from 1966 to 1971, and so on through all the years shown in the table.

e) Make brief comments on any important points you notice in the table.

RSA 1984

5 Regression

INTRODUCTION

1 In this Chapter we consider scattergraphs and relationships between data. From this follows a discussion of a straight line in simple algebraic terms. Finally, the line of best fit (the regression line) is discussed. It is shown how to fit by eye or, for greater accuracy, to fit by formulae.

There are three major parts to this Chapter. They are;

> **Scattergraphs and Relationships**
> **The Straight Line**
> **Fitting a Straight Line To Data**

SCATTERGRAPHS AND RELATIONSHIPS

2 We are familiar with plotting scattergraphs from two sets of data. What we wish to consider now is whether or not there is a relationship between the two set of data. We shall demonstrate this idea by example.

3 It was a lovely Spring morning. Rather cold but sunny. Harry was curious to know how the temperature in his greenhouse was rising. He took five readings from his thermometer at hourly intervals and below is the table of his recorded values;

TIME (Hours)	0	1	2	3	4
TEMPERATURE (^{0}C)	10	12	14	16	18

Harry then plotted this data on a scattergraph as shown

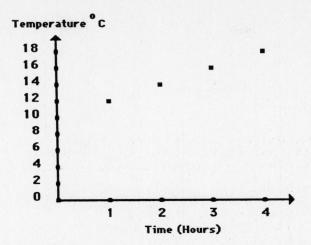

By inspecting this graph Harry realised that he could draw a straight line through all the points on the scattergraph.

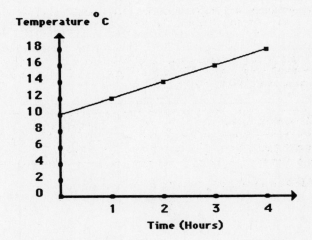

Having done this he could then find out what the intervening temperatures hade been between his recordings . For example, the temperature one and a half an hours after his first reading would have been 13ºC. This number is read off as shown in the following graph;

179

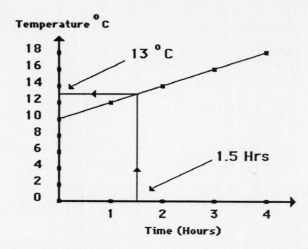

4 This process of obtaining a value that is intermediate to the values recorded is known as INTERPOLATION. We must take care when we interpolate because we are making the assumption that the temperature was rising at the same steady rate bewoen Harry's reading as the staight line seems to show. It is possible that the temperature rose unevenly and that the steady appearance of the temperature rise from the readings was just coincidence.

5 Harry could also EXTEND his graph beyond the last reading and PREDICT that the temperature FIVE hours after he started taking readings was 20°C. This extension is shown below.

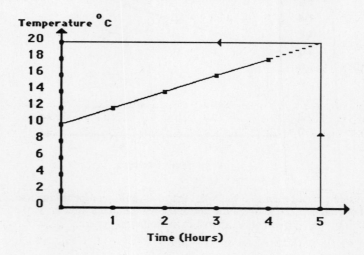

This process of going beyond the recorded data to predict values is known as EXTRAPOLATION.

Again care must be taken when extrapolating data. We are assuming that the steady rise recorded will continue following the same pattern. However, if the sun went in then it is possible that the temperature would remain the same at 18°C.

THE STRAIGHT LINE

6 Looking at Harry's graph a little closer we can see that there is a RELATIONSHIP between the temperature and the time. This can be expressed in the following statement;

$$\textbf{TEMPERATURE} = \textbf{100°C} + \textbf{2 x (TIME IN HOURS)}$$

Denoting the temperature by the symbol **y** and the time by the symbol **x** we can express this relationship by the following equation

$$y = 10 + 2x.$$

To see how this equation works consider the following.

After 3 hours

$$y = 10 + 2 \times 3 = 16°C \qquad \textbf{THIS IS CONFIRMED BY THE DATA}$$

After 3.5 hours

$$y = 10 + 2 \times (3.5) = 17°C \quad \textbf{INTERPOLATION}$$

After 5 hours

$$y = 10 + 2 \times 5 = 20°C \qquad \textbf{EXTRAPOLATION}$$

7 Both the temperature and the time VARY so we call them VARIABLES. The symbols **x** and **y** that we use to represent them are traditional. The variable plotted on the horizontal is traditionally denoted by the letter **x** and the variable plotted on the vertical axis is traditionally denoted by the letter **y**.

The equation

$$y = 10 + 2x$$

is called the EQUATION OF THE STRAIGHT LINE in the above graph. It is a symbolic way of describing the RELATIONSHIP between the time and the temperature.

8 Notice in the above equation, the number 10 is the value of **y** (the temperature) when the value of **x** (the time) is zero. Also the number 2 is the CHANGE in **y** when **x** changes by a UNIT AMOUNT. This is no accident. The general equation for any straight line is given as

$$y = a + bx$$

where **x** and **y** are two variables and **a** and **b** represent two FIXED numbers - in our case 10 and 2 respectively.

9 To conclude we say that the equation

$$y = a + bx$$

is the equation of a straight line plotted on a graph with **x** values plotted on the horizontal axis and **y** values plotted on the vertical axis. The numbers **a** and **b** are two fixed numbers which distinguish one particular line from another. The number **a** is the value of **y** when **x** is zero - the point at which the straight line intersects the vertical axis. The number **b** represents the change in **y** per unit change in **x** - we call it the GRADIENT or SLOPE of the line.

FITTING A STRAIGHT LINE TO DATA

10 The remainder of this Chapter will deal with the processes involved in attempting to fit a straight line to data that has been plotted on a scattergraph. We shall consider;

> **Fitting by eye**
> **Regression by Formulae**
> **Limitations of Regression**

FITTING BY EYE

11 When Harry took the temperature readings in his greenhouse and plotted them on a graph he found that he could draw a straight line through all the points. Let us now suppose the Harry had been too busy to read the thermometer and had asked his friend Bill to do it for him. Unfortunately, Bill is shortsighted and he had left his glasses at home. As a result his temperature readings were not quite as accurate as they should have been. Here are Bill's recordings.

TIME (Hours)	0	1	2	3	4
TEMPERATURE °C	9	13	13	17	17

If we plot this data on a graph we obtain the following;

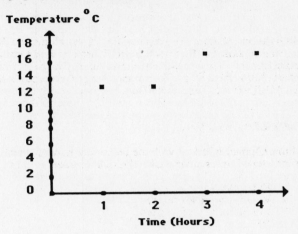

Obviously we cannot draw a single straight line passing through all the points. What we can do is to draw a single straight line that passes closer to these points than any other straight line can. The following graph illustrates this.

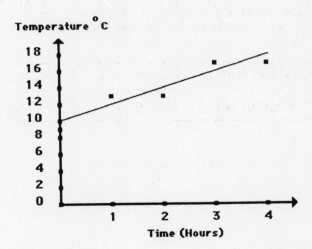

183

12 This line is called the LINE OF BEST FIT - it fits the plotted data better than any other single straight line. Now it so happens that this line of best fit is the same straight line that Harry would have obtained had he read the thermometer. As a result this line of best fit represents the true state of the temperature in the greenhouse. This line of best fit is the line that Bill's plotted points FALL BACK ONTO to obtain the true state of the geenhouse's temperature. The word REGRESS means TO FALL BACK and for this reason the LINE OF BEST FIT is also called the REGRESSION LINE. The REGRESSION LINE is the line that the data points fall back onto *under the assumption that they came from there in the first place*. The reasons why the data points are not actually ON the regression line are many and varied. They could have been incorrectly recorded, as in Bill's case, or the equipment used to obtain them could have been faulty. Whatever the reason there is always the assumption that they SHOULD lie on the regression line and that the regression line represents the ACTUAL RELATIONSHIP.

13 The method of obtaining the regression line for Bill's data is known as FITTING BY EYE   In this case the regression line was obtained accurately. Many times it is not possible to obtain the regression line accurately if we fit by eye. For a more accurate result we can also obtain the regression line by formulae.

REGRESSION BY FORMULAE

14 A factory manufactures engine components and the following table is a record of the profit made for numbers of units sold.   We use the label x to denote the numbers sold in hundreds and the label **y** is used to denote the profit made in thousands of pounds.

Units Sold (100's)	Profit (£1000's)
x	y
1	1
2	3
3	2
4	5
5	3

The following scattergraph is the graphical picture of this data.

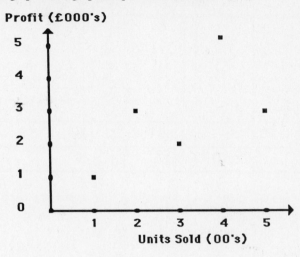

15 The regression line for this data will have an equation of the form

$$y = a + bx$$

where **a** and **b** are the constants we have mentioned before. By means of a mathematical method called **The Method Of Least Squares** it is possible to find the values of **a** and **b** for the regression line (the straight line that best fits this data). It is not appropriate to delve into the Method Of Least Squares here, instead, the results are merely quoted.

$$b = \{n\Sigma xy - (\Sigma x)(\Sigma y)\} \div \{n\Sigma x^2 - (\Sigma x)^2\}$$

$$a = \{\Sigma y - b\Sigma x\} \div n$$

where n is the number of **x-values** (being the same as the number of **y-values**) and where the symbol

$$\Sigma$$

(which is a capital letter S in the Greek Alphabet - it is pronounced SIGMA) stands for **SUM.** So that, for example,

$$\Sigma x$$

means the **SUM** of all the **x-values** and

$$\Sigma xy$$

means the **SUM** of all the **xy** products. In order to apply our data to these formulae we construct the following table.

x	y	x^2	xy
1	1	1	1
2	3	4	6
3	2	9	6
4	5	16	20
5	3	25	15
$\Sigma x = 15$	$\Sigma y = 14$	$\Sigma x^2 = 55$	$\Sigma xy = \cancel{55}\,48$
$(\Sigma xy)^2 = 225$		$n = 5$	

16 Using the sums shown in this table we can now calculate the values of **a** and **b**. Since we need the value of **b** to calculate the value of **a** we calculate **b** first.

$$b = \{5 \times 48 - 15 \times 14\} + \{5 \times 55 - 225\}$$

$$\overset{240}{= \{\cancel{220} - 210\} + \{275 - 225\}}$$

$$\overset{30}{= \cancel{10} + 50}$$

$$= \cancel{0.2}\ 0.6$$

$$a = \{14 - \overset{0.6}{(\cancel{0.2})} \times 15\} + 5$$

$$= \overset{5}{\cancel{11}} + 5$$

$$= \cancel{2.2}\ 1.0$$

The equation of the regression line is then given by the equation

$$\overset{1.0 + 0.6x}{y = \cancel{2.2 + 0.2x}}$$

Plotting this line we see how close a fit it is to the data.

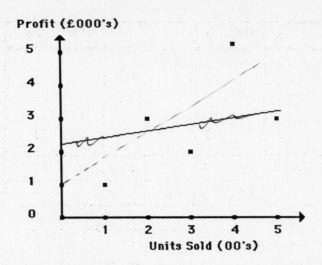

We can see from this graph that the points plotted are quite widely scattered about the regression line. The data from which this regression line was derived were recorded exactly. As a result it would appear that we cannot say the plotted data points are assumed to COME FROM the regression line. This seems to contradict our earlier statement in paragraph 12 that the plotted point *are* assumed to come from the regression line. To reconcile this apparent contradiction we must recognise that the regression line obtained is a plot of AVERAGES. Since the profit increases as the number of units sold increases there is an average profit increase per single extra unit sold. It is in fact £200 which is represented by the number 0.2 which is measured in thousands of pounds. If then the ACTUAL data recorded are considered as contributing to this AVERAGE PROFIT then the data points *will* fall back onto the regression line therby reconciling the apparent contradiction.

LIMITATIONS OF THE REGRESSION LINE

17 We defined the regression line as the line that the data points fall back onto under the assumption that on the line is where they should be. However, we must not assume that the regression line is valid OUTSIDE THE RANGE OF THE DATA. For this reason we can safely interpolate between the extreme values of the data but we cannot extrapolate beyond them. From this example we see that if we do extrapolate to $x = 0$ then we find that $y = 2.2$ - if the factory sells no components at all it makes £2,200 profit! This clearly demonstrates the dangers of extrapolation.

SUMMARY

18 When two sets of data are related to one another the relationship can be demonstrated by plotting one set of data against the other on a scattergraph. Sometimes there is a simple relationship where uniform change in one data value corresponds to a uniform change in the other data value. In such a case a straight line can be drawn through all the plotted data points. It is possible for a relationship of this kind to exist between two data variables that is not directly shown on the scattergraph. In such a situation we construct the straight line that best fits the plotted data. This line of best fit - called the REGRESSION line - can be fitted by eye or, for more accuracy, fitted by formulae.

KEY POINTS TO NOTE

19 Interpolation, Extrapolation, The straight line, Fitting a straight line by eye, Regression by formulae, The Σ notation, Limitations of the regression line.

STUDENT SELF TESTING

SELF REVIEW QUESTIONS

1. What is interpolation? (4)

2. What is extrapolation? (5)

3. Write down the equation for a straight line. (8,9)

4. What does 'regression' mean? (12)

5. What does Σx and Σxy mean? (15)

6. What are the limitations of the regression line? (17)

EXERCISES (Answers begin on Page 249)

1. Is there any evidence of a relation between x and y shown in the following scattergraph?

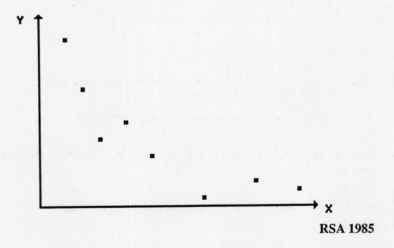

RSA 1985

2.

Year	Private cars with Current Licences (Thousands)
1976	13,792
1977	No data available
1978	13,801
1979	14,307
1980	14,772
1981	14,943
1982	15,303
1983	15,543

a) Round the figures to the nearest hundred thousand.

b) Draw a graph, showing how the rounded figures change with the time (label your graph clearly).

c) Draw, by eye, a regression line on the graph.

d) Estimate the year in which the number of licenced private cars exceeds 16 million. Comment on how reliable your estimate is likely to be.

RSA 1986

3. Ten different colleges, a - k, entered students for examinations in business studies (BS), typewriting (T) and English language (E).

The numbers sitting in Spring 1983 for each college were as follows;

College	a	b	c	d	e	f	g	h	j	k
BS:	15	29	18	12	47	20	55	9	11	23
T:	11	33	18	16	65	32	58	2	18	36
E:	15	9	8	7	12	1	6	8	4	10

With the help of suitable scatter diagrams, discuss whether there appears to be any relationship between the numbers sitting the different subjects.

Suggest possible reasons for any relationship you think exists.

RSA 1984

4. The following table shows the number of staff in each of six regional offices and the total running costs (including salaries) of these offices.

Number of staff	10	8	14	16	11	7
Running costs (£ thousands)	102	93	143	134	121	99

a) Draw a suitable graph to illustrate this information

b) Calculate the equation of the line of regression of total running costs on number of staff and draw it on your graph.

b) Predict the running costs of a regional office employing 12 staff.

LCCI 1984

5. a) Construct a scattergraph for the following data.

x	1	2	3	4	5
y	4	8	9	10	14

b) Draw a line of best fit by eye.

c) Obtain the equation of the regression line.

d) Draw the regression line on the scattergraph and compare with your line of best fit draw by eye.

6 Correlation

INTRODUCTION

1 This Chapter deals with the CORRELATION between two sets of data. CORRELATION is defined and distinguished from CAUSE-AND-EFFECT. The maesurement of correlation is discussed and positive, negative and zero correlation are identified. The correlation between two sets of data is obtained using the Product Moment Correlation Coefficient and the Spearman Rank Correlation Coefficient.

There are four major parts to this Chapter. They are;

> **Correlation**
> **The Amount of Correlation**
> **Measuring Correlation**
> **Limitations of Correlation**

CORRELATION

2 When a change in one quantity is accompanied by change in another quantity then we say that both quantities are CORRELATED.

If you place your finger on a violin string and bow the string then a musical note will be heard. As your finger moves down the string so the pitch of the note rises. The position of your finger on the string and the pitch of the corresponding note are CORRELATED.

3 We must take care not to think in terms of CAUSE-AND-EFFECT when dealing with correlation. Obviously, the position of your finger on the violin string CAUSES THE EFFECT of a certain note. However, correlation and cause-and-effect are two different ideas. For example, during the month of November the average share price on the London Stock Exchange rose in value. during the same period the length of the day decreased. By comparing the average share values and the length of the corresponding day it was found that there was a correlation. A decrease in the length of the day was accompanied by an increase in the average share price. However, no-one would claim there was any cause-and-effect - the average share price did not rise BECAUSE the length of the day decreased. Where there is CAUSE-AND-EFFECT then there will be correlation. However, there can be correlation without cause-and-effect.

THE AMOUNT OF CORRELATION

4 The amount of correlation between two sets of data can range from strong through weak to no correlation at all. If it is possible to predict with certainty the value of one quantity from knowing the value of another quantity then the correlation is STRONG and is said to be PERFECT. For example, the weight of a bucket of water increases with the volume of water in the bucket. There is PERFECT CORRELATION between weight and volume of water. If it is only possible to predict the approximate value of one quantity from a knowledge of another quantity then the correlation between the two quantities ia said to be WEAK. There is a weak correlation between the number of shots at goal and the number of goals scored in a football match. Obviously, the more shots at goal there are the more chance there is of a goal but it is not possible to say that a given number of shots will produce one goal.

5 The following scattergraphs show levels of correlation.

The profit made on the sale of a commodity depends directly on the number of items sold. The first scattergraph illustrates this fact.

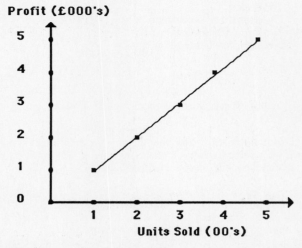

The fact that all the points are confined to the line show that there is PERFECT CORRELATION between units sold and profit.

From the results of a number of football matches the number of shots at goal were recorded against the number of goals scored. From this data the average number of shots at goal were calculated to produce a given number of goals. The following graph is a plot of this data. Here the points are scattered about the line and show that correlation is not strong. The more scattered the points the weaker the correlation.

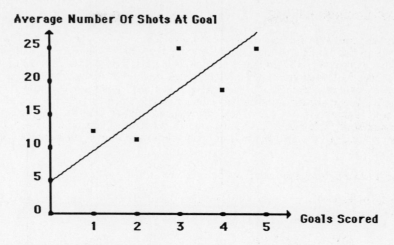

In the third scattergraph the sales of cars is plotted against the daily temperature.

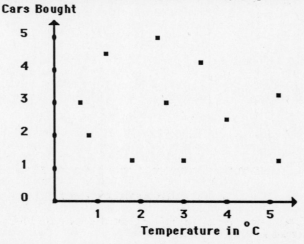

The plotted points on this scattergraph are widely scattered. From this we can deduce that there is no correlation at all between the number of cars bought on any particular day and that day's temperature.

In the final scattergraph we have plotted the pressure of a gas contained in a sealed chamber as the volume of that chamber changes.

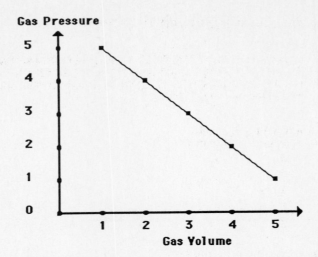

Here again we have perfect correlation. However, since the value of one variable DECREASES as the other INCREASES we must distinguish this perfect correlation from the earlier one. We do so by saying that this perfect correlation is NEGATIVE whereas the previous one was POSITIVE.

MEASURING CORRELATION

6 So far we have used words like strong and weak to relate the amount of correlation possessed by two sets of data. These words are very imprecise and are of little use when presenting the results of a statistical enquiry.

7 It is possible to measure the correlation precisely. When two sets of data are perfectly correlated they possess the greatest amount of correlation. We then say that the two sets of data have a CORRELATION COEFFICIENT of 1 if they INCREASE together. If one INCREASES when the other DECREASES then the correlatation is negative. In this case we say that the CORRELATION COEFFICIENT is -1. The word COEFFICIENT means an ATTRIBUTE which is possessed by both sets of data together. When two sets of data posses no correlation then we say that they have a CORRELATION COEFFICIENT of value 0.

In conclusion, the correlation coefficient of any two sets of data will lie between +1 and -1. We shall now look at two methods of obtaining the correlation coefficient exactly. They are;

The Product Moment Correlation Coefficient
Spearman's Rank Correlation Coefficient

PRODUCT MOMENT CORRELATION COEFFICIENT r

8 By various mathematical manipulations that it is not appropriate to consider here it can be shown that the CORRELATION COEFFICIENT **r** between two sets of data (represented by **x** and **y** values) is given by

$$r = \{n\Sigma xy - (\Sigma x)(\Sigma y)\} \div \{[n\Sigma x^2 - (\Sigma x)^2] \times [n\Sigma y^2 - (\Sigma y)^2]\}^{1/2}$$

This coefficient is called the **Product Moment correlation Coefficient** or the **Pearson Coefficient.** It looks horrendous at first sight but by being methodical it is really quite easy to work out. Let us consider the case of the factory producing engine components that we considered in the previous Chapter. In that Chapter we had the following table

Units Sold (100's) x	Profit (£1000's) y
1	1
2	3
3	2
4	5
5	3

From this table we now construct the following table.

x	y	xy	x^2	y^2
1	1	1	1	1
2	3	6	4	9
3	2	6	9	4
4	5	20	16	25
5	3	15	25	9

$$\Sigma x = \overline{15} \quad \Sigma y = \overline{14} \quad \Sigma xy = \overline{48} \quad \Sigma x^2 = \overline{55} \quad \Sigma y^2 = \overline{48}$$

$$n = 5 \text{ the number of x-values.}$$

Inserting these values into the formula for **r** we obtain

$$r = \{5 \times 48 - 15 \times 14\} \div \{[5 \times 55 - 15 \times 15] \times [5 \times 48 - 14 \times 14]\}^{1/2}$$

$$= \{240 - 210\} \div \{[275 - 225] \times [240 - 196]\}^{1/2}$$

$$= 30 \div \{50 \times 44\}^{1/2}$$

$$= 30 \div 46.91$$

$$= 0.64$$

There is a reasonable amount of correlation between sales and profits as we would expect.

SPEARMAN'S RANK CORRELATION COEFFICIENT r_s

9 Instead of calculating the correlation coefficient from the actual data values it is possible to rank the data in order of size and calculate the correlation from the ranking. In this case we use the formula for the Spearman Rank Correlation Coefficient r_s

$$r_s = 1 - \{6\Sigma d^2\} + \{n(n^2 - 1)\}$$

where **n** is the number of data items and **d** is the **DIFFERENCE** between corresponding data in the ranked series. For example, Eric and Richard are two salesmen selling Stationery. Their sales figures for last month are recorded in the following table.

Stationery Sales	Value of Sales (£)	
	Richard	Eric
Paper A4	1200	400
Pens	600	1000
Folders	800	700
Typewriter Ribbons	2100	1800
Printing Ink	750	1200

In the table that follows the sales values are ranked according to size where 1 represents the highest sale, 2 the next highest and so on.

Ranked Sales Value	Ranked Sales		Difference	
	Richard	Eric	d	d^2
Paper A4	2	5	-3	9
Pens	5	3	+2	4
Folders	3	4	-1	1
Typewriter Ribbons	1	1	0	0
Printing Ink	4	2	+2	4
			$\Sigma d^2 = 18$	
n = 5 : n^2 = 25				

Applying these results to Spearman's formula we obtain

$$r_s = 1 - \{6 \times 18\} + \{5 \times (25 - 1)\}$$

$$= 1 - (108 + 120)$$

$$= 1 - 0.9$$

$$= 0.1$$

This low number shows that there is very little correlation between Eric's and Richard's sales. Just because Richard sells a lot of one particular item does not mean that Eric will do so as well.

THE LIMITATIONS OF CORRELATION

10 Correlation is not a good indicator of a causal connection. There may be a known indirect causal connection between two sets of data that have a high correlation. There may then be a temptation to assume a more direct causal connection but yielding to this temptation could result in wrong conclusions. Furthermore, there may be a very high correlation between two unrelated sets of data. For these reasons it would be most unwise to use correlation as a basis for prediction.

11 The reliability of the coefficients r and r_s increases as the number of data items increase. Very little reliance should be placed on the values of r and r_s for small numbers of data items.

SUMMARY

12 Two sets of data are said to be CORRELATED when a change in one set is accompanied by a change in the other set. If they both increase or decrease together they have a POSITIVE correlation. If one increases as the other decreases they have a NEGATIVE correlation. Correlation should not be confused with CAUSE-AND-EFFECT, they are two quite distinct ideas. If there is a cause-and-effect between two sets of data then they will be strongly correlated. However, it is also possible to have a strong correlation between two quite different types of data where there is no causal connection. This occurs by coincidence. Correlation can be measured accurately by using either the Product Moment Correlation Coefficient or Spearman's Rank Correlation Coefficient. The Product Moment Correlation Coefficient is calculated directly from the data values. To obtain the Spearman's Rank Correlation Coefficient the data must be ranked in order of size. This coefficient is then calculated from the differences in the rankings. This latter method is very useful when trying to find the correlation between two non-measurable attributes.

KEY POINTS TO NOTE

13 Correlation, Cause-and-effect, Perfect correlation, Negative correlation, Correlation coefficients, Limitations of correlation

STUDENT SELF TESTING

SELF REVIEW QUESTIONS

1. What is the meaning of correlation? (2)

2. What is the connection between correlation and cause-and-effect? (3)

3. What is perfect correlation? (4,5)

4. What is negative correlation? (5)

5. What is meant by a correlation coefficient? (7)

6. What is the range of values of a correlation coefficient? (7)

7. What are the limitations of correlation? (10,11)

EXERCISES (Answers begin on Page 249)

1. What is meant by correlation? The following data are available from a study of the output of a firm and the number of defective items. Calculate a correlation coefficient from the information.

Output per Day (No. Of Items)	Number of Defective Items
103	14
96	12
100	12
115	15
126	17

LCCI 1981

2. The following table shows the number of staff and the value of sales in a particular week for each of seven stores.

Number of Staff	6	11	12	9	11	7	9
Value of Sales (£ thousands)	21	18	33	39	25	27	21

a) Draw a suitable graph to illustrate this data.

b) Calculate the value of the product moment correlation coefficient for the data.

c) Without further calculation, interpret the value obtained in part b)

LCCI 1985

3. Five branches of a store were ranked three times, firstly according to sales, secondly according to quality and thirdly according to price. The rankings are listed below;

Branch	Sales	Quality	Price
A	2	5	1
B	4	1	3
C	1	2	2
D	3	3	4
E	5	4	5

Obtain rank correlation coefficients to decide whether price or quality is likely to be more important for sales.

The rank correlation coefficient between quality and price is -0.1. What does this mean?

4. Ten candidates for an administrative post were ranked by the two members of the interviewing panel in the following manner;

Panel	1	4	2	7	1	5	6	9	3	10	8
Members	2	3	2	5	1	4	9	6	7	8	10

Calculate Spearman's rank correlation coefficient and discuss whether it represents a measure of agreement between the two panel members.

LCCI 1983

5. The price of a particular commodity was reduced by different percentages in different branches of a store. The percentage change in subsequent sales were recorded in the following table.

Price Cut %	5	7	10	14	20
Sales Change %	3	4	8	8	10

Calculate the product moments correlation coefficient and comment on the result.

7 Time Series

INTRODUCTION

1 This Chapter deals with data that is recorded over a period of time. Such data form TIME SERIES. The short term variations in the time series are considered and they are distinguished from the long term tendency. The TREND is defined. It is shown how to obtain the trend by using the method of MOVING AVERAGES. SEASONAL FACTORS are derived and the DE-SEASONALISING of future data is demonstrated. Finally, the use of time series as a predictive tool is considered.

There are five major parts to this Chapter. They are;

> **Time Series**
> **Use of Time Series**
> **Moving averages and the Trend**
> **Seasonal Factors**
> **Predictions**

TIME SERIES

2 A TIME SERIES is the name given to data collected over a period of time. The data consists of the value of some quantity and the time at which it was collected. The time can be given in hours, days, months or even years - it all depends upon the nature of the problem. For example, the following table records the daily takings of a bus conductor during one week.

DAY	Mon	Tue	Wed	Thu	Fri
TAKINGS (£)	278	304	325	269	324

This record is a typical TIME SERIES.

With data in this form it is natural to plot a graph of time against takings. We traditionally plot the time horizontally and the other variable vertically. Below is the graph of the time series recorded above.

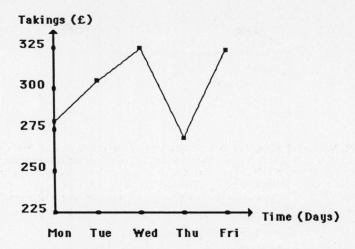

Notice that the data consists of 5 pairs of numbers. These 5 pairs of numbers are plotted as points and then each point is joined to its neighbour by a straight line. Jagged-line graphs are typical of time series.

USES OF TIME SERIES

3 The purpose of collecting time series data is to enable us to PREDICT future events. A dress shop may notice that each week the number of trousers that is sells is decreasing. By a careful analysis of quantity sold over a period of time the dress shop owner may be able to predict how many tousers she will expect to sell next month. She will then be able to make sure that she does not buy in more trousers than she can sell.

When the quantity of trousers sold decreases steadily each week it is fairly safe to predict that next week the quantity sold will decrease again. However, in most real-life situations the problems are more involved. For example, the following table records the monthly amounts of smokeless fuel sold by a coal merchant over the period of two years.

Smokeless Fuel Sales	Year 1	Year 2
	(Tonnes)	
January	120	110
February	140	125
March	115	98
April	95	80
May	70	81
June	60	38
July	40	22
August	35	14
September	60	18
October	74	63
November	110	92
December	135	120

A graph of this data is given below

Graph of Coal Merchant's Smokeless Fuel Sales

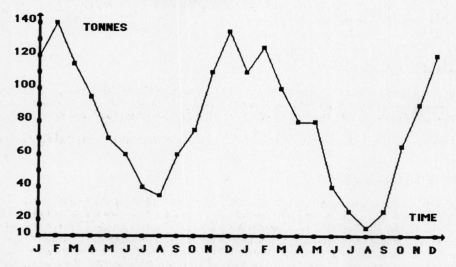

4 It can be seen that the graph of this time series varies with troughs and peaks every few months. Indeed the troughs and peaks occur quite regularly but at the same time there is a steady tendency for the graph to fall. Here we must distinguish between two properties of times series, namely

The short term variation
The long term tendency

THE SHORT TERM VARIATION

5 The short term variation is the rise and fall of the graph over periods of time that are short compared with the total time scale of the graph This short term variation is displayed as a series of troughs and peaks. The causes of short term variations can be separated into three categories;

> **Seasonal Fluctuations**
> **Cyclical Fluctuations**
> **Residual Fluctuations**

SEASONAL FLUCTUATIONS

6 Data can vary regularly due to seasonal influences. For example, less fuel is bought in summer than in winter. Such variations in the data that occur regularly are called SEASONAL FLUCTUATIONS. But be careful about the name SEASON. It does not necessarily refer to the annual seasons. If we find regular fluctuations of a commodity over the short term period of a week then these fluctuations are still called SEASONAL. The essential feature of a seasonal fluctuation is that it is REGULAR.

CYCLICAL FLUCTUATIONS

7 Data can vary because certain influences are felt at certain times in a semi-regular manner. Business activity is affected by boom and slump and these two effects occur with regularity but not at specified, regular time intervals. This sort of up and down variation that is not regular in time is called a CYCLICAL FLUCTUATION.

RESIDUAL FLUCTUATIONS

8 Any variation in the data that is neither seasonal nor cyclic is called RESIDUAL. Such fluctuations can be caused by catastrophic events such as fire or flood. They can also be caused by more predictable but still random events such as labour disputes or extreme weather conditions.

In this book the only variations in the data that we shall consider in detail are seasonal fluctuations.

THE LONG TERM TENDENCY

9 We saw in the last example that the sale of the smokeless fuel had a regular variation over the short term. we also saw that over the two year period there was a tendency for the sales to INCREASE. This LONG TERM TENDENCY is called the TREND. In our example the TREND is for the sales to increase. However, just by looking at the data or the graph it is imposible to quantify this trend. The trend is mixed up with the seasonal variations. In order to quantify the trend we must separate it from the seasonal variations. We do this by using the method of MOVING AVERAGES that we considered in Chapter 1 of this Section.

MOVING AVERAGES AND THE TREND

10 We shall illustrate the separation of the trend from the seasonal variations by using an example.

Liz was a buyer for McHenry's - a chain of fast food outlets. McHenry's specialised in their hamburgers and claimed to sell millions each week. One of Liz's responsibilities was to purchase each month the beef that went into the hamburgers at six particular outlets. Last January Liz was posed a problem. She was offered a large consignment of beef provided that she paid for it in January and took delivery in April. Ordinarily Liz would not have taken any notice of such an offer but this time the price of the beef was incredibly low. Unfortunately the consignment was large enough at 2000 Kilo to cover at least three months of beef usage. This was her problem. Should she buy the 2000 Kilo of beef and thereby dramatically *increase* the profits? But what if the beef did not all sell in the three months? The cost of storing the beef was so high that if she did not sell it all in three months she may incur extra storage costs and thereby dramatically *decrease* the profits.

11 Before Liz could make a decision she had to have some idea of how much beef she could be expected to need during next April, May and June. To enable her to make this prediction she had to make a record of the beef used for each three month (quarterly) period for the past three years. Below is a table that contains this record.

MacHenry's Beef Usage	(Kilo)		
	Year 1	Year 2	Year 3
1st Quarter	1240	1460	1680
2nd Quarter	1020	1300	1670
3rd Quarter	830	1050	1440
4th Quarter	1150	1320	1800

From this table Liz produced the following graph

Graph Of Beef Usage

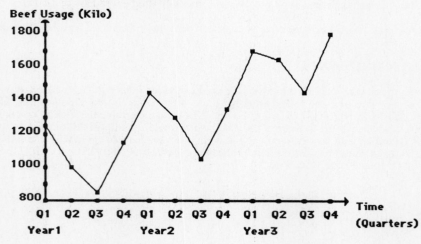

As can be seen the graph appears to have an upward trend. However, this trend is mixed up with a seasonal fluctuation that repeats itself every year. In order to even out these seasonal fluctuations Liz has three options

Draw a line of best fit by eye
Draw a line using regression
Draw a line using the method of moving averages

DRAWING A TREND LINE OF BEST FIT BY EYE

12 This option was rejected because the line would be curved and would produce predictions that were not accurate enough.

DRAWING A TREND LINE BY REGRESSION

13 Liz could have managed this if the line had been straight. Unfortunately her mathematics was inadequte to cope with curved regression lines and so this option was ruled out.

DRAWING A TREND LINE USING THE METHOD OF MOVING AVERAGES

14 This is the option that Liz chose. The principle of using the method of moving averages is that the seasonal fluctuations are evened out over one short term period at a time. This short term period is the time over which the data falls from a maximum to a minimum and then rises back to a maximum. From the data collected by Liz it can be seen that this period is a year. As a consequence Liz found the moving average for successive yearly or four-quarterly periods. This is done in the following table.

Moving Averages And Seasonal Variations

Quarter	Weight	4 Quarter Total	Moving Average	Centered Average	Variations
Q1	1240				
Q2	1020				
		4240	1060		
Q3	830			1088	-258
		4460	1115		
Q4	1150			1150	0
		4740	1185		
Q1	1460			1213	247
		4960	1240		
Q2	1300			1262	38
		5130	1283		
Q3	1050			1311	-261
		5350	1338		
Q4	1320			1384	-64
		5720	1430		
Q1	1680			1479	201
		6110	1528		
Q2	1670			1588	82
		6590	1648		
Q3	1440				
Q4	1800				

15 As we see this table consists of six columns. Columns 1 and 2 contain the data collected by Liz, namely the quarter and the amount of beef used during that quarter. The 3rd column contains the sum of beef used during four successive quarters. For example, the beef used in the first year is 4240 Kilos. The next number below this is the sum of the beef used during the last three quarters of the first year and the first quarter of the second year. The remainder of this column is obtained in the same manner, by subtracting the first quarter's usage in the previous sum and adding the next quarter's usage. The numbers in this column are the MOVING TOTALS for consequetive four-quarter periods. The 4th column contains the MOVING AVERAGES for consequetive four-quarter periods. Each number in this column is equal to the adjacent number in the previous column divided by 4. These averages represent the average quarterly usage of beef during a year - in this way the seasonal fluctuations have been averaged out.

16 From the spacings in the table we see that the moving avereages are centered BETWEEN TWO QUARTERS. In other words the moving averages do not correspond in time to the time that the beef usage refers. Because of this we CENTER the moving averages to make them so correspond. The 5th column is the AVERAGE OF THE TWO NEAREST MOVING AVERAGES in the 4th column. These CENTERED MOVING AVERAGES are now positioned directly opposite a particular quarters usage. This now allows us to complete the 6th column which contains the difference between the quarterly beef usages and the corresponding moving average for that quarter. If we had not centered the moving averages as we did then these numbers could not have been obtained.
The numbers in the 5th column represents the TREND and this can now be plotted on a graph as shown.

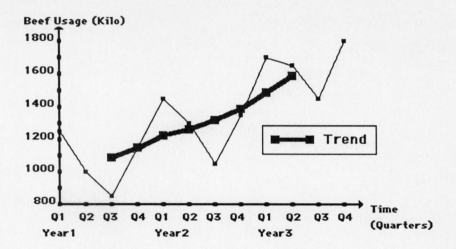

SEASONAL FACTORS

17 The TREND is the time series data with the SEASONAL FLUCTUATIONS averaged out. In obtaining the trend as we have done we have DE-SEASONALISED the original data. The variations in column 6 of the table represent the SEASONAL FACTORS that de-seasonalise the original data. For example, The low usage of 830 in quarter 3 of the first year is de-seasonlised by adding to it the variation 258 in column 6 to obtain 1088. The high usage 1680 in quarter 1 of the third year is de-seasonalised by subtracting the variation 201 to obtain 1479. This is the effect of de-seasonalising - low usage in one quarter is balanced against high usage in another quarter by adding and subtracting the appropriate SEASONAL FACTORS.

18 This principle will now allow us to de-seasonalise any future data. Each quarter in a year has a seasonal factor associated with it. This factor can then be added or subtracted from any future quarters usage thereby de-seasonalising it. Unfortunately, looking at the seasonal factors in column six we see that they are all different so which ones should we use? What we really require are just four seasonal factors that can be applied during the approriate quarter in any year. We achieve this by averaging the variations in column six.

In the following table the variations are given against the appropriate year and quarter.

Seasonal Factors	Quarter 1	Quarter 2	Quarter 3	Quarter 4
Year 1	–	–	-258	0
Year 2	247	38	-261	-64
Year 3	201	82	–	–
TOTAL	448	120	-519	-64
AVERAGE	224	60	-260	-32 (-8)
ADJUSTMENT	+2	+2	+2	+2
FACTORS	226	62	-258	-30

The TOTAL row consists of the sum of the variations above and the AVERAGE row contains their average - the sum of the variations divided by the number of variations in the sum. These are the four unadjusted SEASONAL FACTORS.

19 If the average seasonal fluctuations are added together their sum equals -8 (the number in brackets at the end of the AVERAGE row). We require seasonal factors that add up to zero so that over a complete year they cancel each other out. If the seasonal factors do not add up to zero their non-zero sum would be added to the trend. This would mean that they were not purely seasonal factors but contained additive factors as well. To achieve a zero sum we add +8 in four equal parts of 2 to each quarter's average. This gives the final row of adjusted seasonal factors whose sum *is* zero. Notice that to take the seasonal effect out of the quarterly data we must SUBTRACT the seasonal factors - this is the process of DE-SEASONALISING THE DATA.

PREDICTIONS

20 Liz could now use both the trend line and the seasonal factors to predict her anticipated usage of beef during next April, May and June. If we refer to the original table we can see that in column 5 the trend falls short of the data by TWO quarters. By using the seasonal factors for these quarters we can de-seasonalise them.

In the 3rd quarter of year 3 the beef usage was 1440 Kilo. The 3rd quarter seasonal factor is -258 Kilo which we SUBTRACT from the actual usage in order to de-seasonalise it. The same applies to the following quarter's 1800 Kilo beef usage. This must be de-seasonalised by SUBTRACTING -30 Kilo. Thus,

$$1440 - (-258) = 1440 + 258$$

$$= 1698 \quad \text{(3rd Quarter)}$$

$$1800 - (-30) = 1800 + 30$$

$$= 1830 \quad \text{(4th Quarter)}$$

The complete trend is now plotted on the following graph

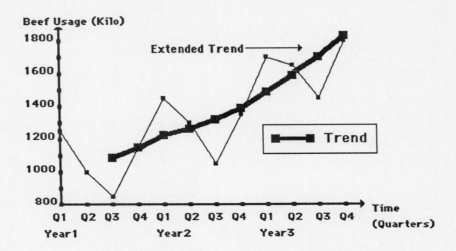

We see that for the last two years the trend line more or less follows a smooth curve. We now project this curve by two quarters where the extension follows naturally from what has gone before.

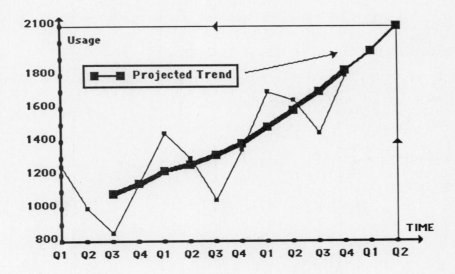

The projection represents the PREDICTION of future usage of beef over the next two quarters. This prediction is made against past usage and the reasonable expectation that the pattern in the graph will continue.

Reading off the second predicted quarters usage we see that 2100 Kilo of beef is expected to be used during that 2nd quarter. Now we must remember that this number comes from the trend line which is a plot of de-seasonalised data. To obtain the predicted ACTUAL beef usage for the 2nd Quarter we must seasonalise it by the seasonal factor for that quarter. This means that we must ADD the seasonal factor of 62 Kilo.

$$2100 + 62 = 2160 \text{ Kilo}$$

Since Liz had been offered 2000 Kilo of Beef she accepted the offer and looked forward to a substantial increase in profits during that quarter.

CAUTION

21 Using time series to make predictiions in this way requires the exercise of caution. There are two assumptions that have been made that we must be aware of, namely

> **Continuance of the trend pattern**
> **No residual or cyclical fluctuations expected**

CONTINUANCE OF THE TREND PATTERN

22 We are assuming that future behaviour will follow the same pattern as past behaviour. In many situations this can be a reasonable assumption but there is a limit to how far into the future we can go.

NO RESIDUAL OR CYCLICAL FLUCTUATIONS EXPECTED

23 We are assuming that influences other than seasonal influences will not occur during the period of our prediction. This assumptiom must be made with careful consideration of future possibilities. For example, if the weather is likely to affect the figures then abnormal weather could seriously upset the prediction. Always remeber Murphy's Law - "If it can go wrong then it will". When making this second assumption always try to foresee any event whose occurrence could seriously affect the prediction.

SUMMARY

24 A TIME SERIES is a set of data collected over a period of time. The purpose of generating time series is to allow the accurate prediction of future events. Time series contain short term variations and a long term trend. The short term variations are seasonal, cyclical or residual. A trend line can be fitted to a scattergraph of the time series data by eye or be regression formulae. Fitting by eye is unsatisfactory as it is inaccurate. Fitting by regression formulae becomes very difficult if the line of best fit is a curve. A third method using moving averages is generally used to obtain the trend line. The trend line represents the time series data with the short term variations averaged out. In the case of data containing only seasonal variations the method of moving averages produces SEASONAL FACTORS. The seasonal factors are used to de-seasonalise the data. When using the trend line to predict future events we must assume that the trend pattern will continue. This is usually a reasonable assumption provided we do not project too far into the future. When predicting from the trend line we must also try to forsee any possible events that may introduce un-catered for short term variations.

KEY POINTS TO NOTE

25 Time series, Uses of time series, Short term variations, Long term tendency, trend, Moving averages, Seasonal factors, De-seasonalising data, Predictions

STUDENT SELF TESTING

SELF REVIEW QUESTIONS

1. What is a time series? (2)

2. What is a time series used for? (3)

3. List two type of variation in a time series. (4)

4. List three types of short term variation. (5)

5. What is a seasonal fluctuation? (6)

6. What is meant by a season? (6)

7. What are cyclical fluctuations? (7)

8. What are residual fluctuations? (8)

9. Give another name for the long term tendency. (9)

10. What is the trend line? (10,11)

11. List three possible ways of obtaining the trend line. (11)

12. What is a seasonal factor? (17)

13. How is data de-seasonalised? (18)

14. What factors must be assumed in order to use the trend line to predict? (20,21)

EXERCISES (Answers begin on Page 249)

1. The quarterly index numbers of the retail price of a particular commodity are recorded for four years.

Quarter	1984	1985	1986	1987
1	295	257	255	255
2	283	284	254	260
3	266	251	255	249
4	265	261	258	261

Calculate the trend and the four seasonal fluctuations.

2. The following table shows the number of houses sold by a firm of estate agents.

	Quarter			
	I	II	III	IV
1981	135	198	182	156
1982	112	181	158	131
1983	88	164	143	107

a) Use the method of moving averages to find the trend.

b) Use the additive model to find the seasonal variations.

c) Use the results from a) and b) to predict the sales in the first quarter of 1984

LCCI 1985

3. A coach company recorded the number of hirings of its coaches in the following table.

	Quarter			
	I	II	III	IV
1985	35	52	83	43
1986	42	57	85	43
1987	41	61	92	45

a) Find the trend and the seasonal adjustments

b) Forecast the number of hirings for the first two quarters of 1988.

4.
        Sales of Microcomputers
         By Value (£000's)

| | **Quarters** | | | |
	I	**II**	**III**	**IV**
1979	77.5	63.2	54.8	78.5
1980	80.2	66.0	59.3	84.7
1981	83.8	68.4	62.1	90.3

Using the method of moving averages, find the trend from the above data and, after extracting the seasonal deviations (by use of the additive method), forecast the sales by value for the first two quarters of 1982.

                                                       LCCI 1983

214

Section 5 Communicating The Results

This last section covers the final part of any statistical enquiry - the presentation of the results. Having spent so much effort collecting and analysing data it is most important that this effort is not wasted by a poor display of the conclusions. In this Section we look at the reasons for and the methods of communicating results.

There are four Chapters in this Section. They are;

Chapter 1. The General Principles of Presentation
Chapter 2. Demonstration Tables
Chapter 3. Pictorial Representation
Chapter 4. The Use Of Words

1 The General Principles of Presentation

INTRODUCTION

1 This Chapter gives an overview of the general principles employed when presenting the results of a statistical enquiry. Once the reasons for presenting results have been established the means of presenting them are reviewed. Results are presented by tables, pictures and words.

There are four major parts to this Chapter. They are;

> **The Purposes of Presenting Results**
> **Demonstration Tables**
> **Pictures**
> **Words**

THE PURPOSES OF PRESENTING RESULTS

2 Before deciding how to present the results of a statistical enquiry it is necessary to know why and to whom the results are to be presented. The conclusions of a statistical enquiry are presented for one of three reasons;

> **To demonstrate facts**
> **To support an argument**
> **To influence decisions**

DEMONSTRATING FACTS

3 A statistical enquiry may be conducted simply to provide information. The enquiry conducted by West Linton High School in Section 1 is an example of this. The students found that the average number of pets owned by the households of the local estate increased as the number of children in the household increased. This result was purely informative for presentation to a general audience.

SUPPORTING AN ARGUMENT

4 More usually an enquiry will be undertaken to support an argument between people with a common understanding of a problem. If you have a job that involves spending money in the execution of your duties you may find, one year that you have not been given sufficient funds. To persuade your employers that your department was under-funded you could mount a statistical enquiry into the demands placed upon your funds. In this case you will present your conclusions to support your argument to people who are familiar with the details of your problem. This presentation would undoubtedly require more fine detail than a presentation that was aimed at simply demonstrating facts to a wider audience.

INFLUENCING DECISIONS

5 A statistical enquiry can be mounted to provide persuasive evidence to a mixture of people who are unfamiliar and people who are familiar with the details of a problem. A Local Community Action Group concerned about the pollution of a river by a Chemical Factory might wish to organise a petition to lobby their Member of Parliament. In order to persuade the general public to sign the petition they will have to demonstrate evidence of increasing pollution. Here, their presentation must take into account that the general public are unfamiliar with the details of the problem. At the same time they are going to have to convince people who are in the position of being able to make decisions. Consequently, their presentation to the Member of Parliament must have sufficient detail to support their argument.

6 In all three situations the presentation of results should follow the same general principles. The results must be presented in an easily understood form. Furthermore, the presentation should be short and to the point. The best way to achieve this is to use a combination of

> **Demonstration Tables**
> **Pictures**
> **Words**

DEMONSTRATION TABLES

7 Demonstration tables differ from reference tables in that they are not used to store data but to display it. The data they display consists of

> **Summary Data**
> **Conclusive Data**

SUMMARY DATA

8 Summary data consists of rounded data, totals, averages and percentages obtained from the data in the original reference table. As its name suggests, this data SUMMARISES all the data collected.

CONCLUSIVE DATA

9 Conclusive data consists of totals, averages and percentages obtained from the summary data. It represents the conclusions of a statistical enquiry. The following table is an example of a demonstration table.

Student Enrollment				
Numbers	**BTEC**	**HND**	**BSc**	**TOTAL**
1985/86	28	32	45	105
1986/87	54	68	87	209
1987/88	82	114	138	334
Percentages				
1985/86	27	30	43	100
1986/87	26	33	41	100
1987/88	25	34	41	100

Here the body of the table consists of four columns and two blocks of three rows of numbers. The first three rows and three columns of numbers have been obtained from the primary data collected by a Polytechnic Department of Computing. This is the SUMMARY DATA - it concerns the total student enrollment on three courses in Information Technology that were started in 1985. The last column consists of totals row by row and represents the total number of students in all three courses. The second block of three rows contain the percentages of each year's students on each course. The last column and the second block of three rows are the CONCLUSIVE DATA and are obtained from the summary data. Notice how the fourth column is separated from the preceding three columns by a bold line. This gives a visual division between the two types of data. However, there is no line separating the two blocks of rows. Too many lines in a table can make the table over fussy. Instead we have relied on a spatial break between these two blocks to provide adequate separation.

Demonstration tables should be simple, clear and easily understood. Simplicity and clarity is achieved by keeping the data displayed to a minimum. Ease of comprehension is achieved by a clearly labelled table following all the principles laid down previously when we discussed reference tables.

PICTURES

10 Pictures, which includes graphs, can convey a large amount of complex information quickly and efficiently. They give a visual impact to the data that is presented in the demonstration table.

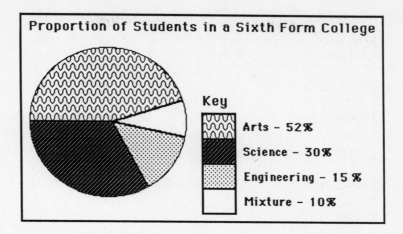

This picture is a good example. It is called a PIE CHART because it looks like a pie that has been cut into portions. Each portion of the pie represents a proportion of all the students in a sixth form college who are studying pareticular types of courses. Pictures should have eye-appeal and should reinforce the message given in a demonstration table.

WORDS

11 A written summary of the conclusions should always accompany the tables and pictures. This should repeat and reinforce the conclusions previously displayed. The summary should be in close proximity to the tables and pistures so that together they form a coherent whole. It should be concise, clearly understood and present the final rounding of the conclusions.

SUMMARY

12 The results of a Statistical Enquiry should be presented in three ways. Firstly, the summary and conclusive data is presented in a table. Secondly these numbers are given a visual reinforcement by a picture. Finally the conclusions are drawn together in a short written summary. All three parts of the presentation must be concise, clear and easily understood.

KEY POINTS TO NOTE

13 Demonstrating facts, Supporting an argument, Influencing decisions, Demonstration tables, Summary data, Conclusive data, Pictures, Words

STUDENT SELF TESTING

SELF REVIEW QUESTIONS

1. List three reasons for presenting the conclusions of a Statistical Enquiry. (2-5)

2. List three methods of presenting results. (6)

3. What is the difference between summary data and conclusive data? (7-9)

4. Why do we use pictures? (10)

5. Why do we use words? (11)

EXERCISES (Answers begin on Page 249)

The following data represents the annual sales of Gears, Valves and Pumps by a large Engineering Manufacturing Company.

	Sales (£)		
	Gears	**Valves**	**Pumps**
1981	121,400	26,500	284,100
1982	152,600	31,200	586,200
1983	133,400	15,400	821,500

1. Simplify this table by rounding the data to two significant figures.

2 Construct a demonstration table which includes the total annual sales for each year and the percentage that each year's total forms of the total three year's sales.

3. Write a short description of the result.

4. Draw a pie chart that contrasts total sales for each of the three years as a proportion of the three year total.

2 Demonstration Tables

INTRODUCTION

1 This Chapter details the elements of constructing Demonstration Tables.

There are three major parts to this Chapter. they are;

> **The Purpose of a Demonstration Table**
> **The Contents of the Table**
> **The Layout of the Table**

THE PURPOSE OF A DEMONSTRATION TABLE

2 The purpose of a demonstration table is to convey a numerical message. That message is the result of a statistical enquiry and it must be conveyed in the most effective way possible. To ensure this we must tkae considerable care over

> **The contents of the table**
> **The layout of the table**

THE CONTENTS OF THE TABLE

3 A Demonstration table contains SUMMARISED DATA derived from the original data. The original data which is tabulated in reference tables does not appear in a demonstration table. The conclusions of the enquiry are contained within the summarised data and to display it effectively it must not be crowded in as an adjunct to the original data. Furthermore, the data in the table must be rounded to two or at most three signifcant figures. The following table contains data that has not been rounded

Table of fish sold by a wholesaler

FISH	WEIGHT (lbs)
Cod	1534
Hake	1226
Mackerel	159
Skate	1674

Here the data is too detailed for a demonstration table. A better display is as follows;

FISH	WEIGHT (100lbs)
Cod	15
Hake	12
Mackerel	2
Skate	17

This display is simple and conveys the pattern in the data more effectively than the first table. We must at all times be aware of our audience. When constructing a demonstration table we must also be aware that the layout of the table ia just as important as the content.

THE LAYOUT OF THE TABLE

4 When confronted with a table of numbers a reader's interest will only be maintained if the numbers are few and are clearly displayed. To achieve this we must create a table that has

> **A columnar display**
> **Visual simplicty**
> **Clear Title and footnotes**

COLUMNAR DISPLAY

5 As with reference tables, the demonstration table must have its entries in clearly defined columns and rows. The rules for labelling columns and rows are the same as discussed for reference tables. It is also important that the data be arranged in some sort of logical order. Remember that this table is to be read as a whole so it must read well. If within the table there are rows or columns containing conclusive figures then these should be clearly distinguished from the rest of the table. This can be done by using bold lines, either horizontal or vertical, to indicate that the numbers in that row or column are significant.

VISUAL SIMPLICITY

6 The boundaries of the columns and rows must be clearly perceived. The entries given to 2 or 3 significant figures only. Any column containing decimal numbers should have the entries located so that the decimal points all come under each other.

TITLE AND FOOTNOTES

7 The same rules apply here as apply to reference tables. The title must be short and easily understood. The footnotes contain any comments that are required to explain special features of the data. Also the sources of the data are given on the footnotes.

SUMMARY

8 Demonstration Tables are used to present the results of a statistical enquiry in numerical form. The construction of the table follows the same rules as the construction of reference tables. The data contained is rounded to 2 or 3 significant figures. The table should present a clear, easily understood display of numbers where any pattern is immediately recognised.

KEY POINTS TO NOTE

9 Contents of a demonstration table, Layout of a demonstration table, Visual simplicity

STUDENT SELF TESTING

SELF REVIEW QUESTIONS

1. What is the purpose of a demonstration table? (2)

2. What does a demonstration table contain? (3)

3. List three features of the layout of a demonstration table. (4)

4. How many significant figures should be used for the entries of a demonstration table? (6)

EXERCISES (Answers begin on Page 249)

1. The total number of employees in a certain trading company is 1,000 and these are arranged in three departments, viz. production, administration and sales. 600 people are employed in the production department and 300 in administration. There are 110 male juveniles in employment, 110 female juveniles and 290 adult females. The remaining employees are adult males.

In the production department there are 350 adult males, 150 adult females and 50 male juveniles, whilst in the administration department there are 100 adult males, 110 adult females and 50 juvenile males.

Draw up a table to show all the details of employment in the company and its departments and provide suitable secondary statistics to describe the distribution of people indepartments

LCCI 1982

2. The following table shows the population of England and Wales, in thousands, in various age-groups for the years 1951, 1961, 1971, 1981.

Age Group	1951	1961	1971	1981
Under 5	3718	3597	3905	2910
5 - 14	5974	6987	7671	7053
15 - 29	8912	8925	10236	10859
30 - 44	9767	9263	8593	9541
45 - 64	10563	11836	11849	10884
65 - 74	3257	3520	4178	4488
75 and over	1568	1976	2318	2786

Source: *Office of Population Censuses and Statistics*

For the years 1951 and 1981, round off the population figures to the nearest hundred thousand, and present them in a table; include the total population size in each year. Give your table a clear heading and label it clearly.

RSA 1985

3. On a new housing estate there are 5,000 properties. 2,000 are bungalows and 1,000 are detached houses - the remaining properties are semi-detached houses. Proprties have either 2 or 3 or 4 bedrooms; thus 100 of the detached houses have 4 bedrooms and none of the bungalows has this number of bedrooms, 500 of the bungalows have 3 bedrooms, whilst none of the detached houses has only 2 bedrooms. There are 2,400 properties with 3 bedrooms on the estate, and 600 properties have 4 bedrooms.

Draw up a suitable table to show the data consciely and calculate suitable secondary statistics to illustrate the composition if the estate.

LCCI 1981

4. A survey was made of cars parked in car-parks of a town. for each car, a record was made of whether it was British-made (B) or made by a foreign manufacturer (F). Its age was also recorded in years (using the single letter in the registration number). Thus B1 stands for a car up to 1 year old made by a British manufacturer.

The results of surveying 120 vehicles were as follows;

B6	F10	F1	B1	B2	B2	F10	F11	B1	B5
B9	B1	B6	B8	F6	B9	F2	F4	F2	B10
F8	B6	F5	B4	F1	B2	F3	B12	F7	B8
B5	B1	B3	B5	F9	B2	F5	F3	B9	F7
F9	F3	B8	B10	B7	F7	F1	B1	B3	F1
B12	B6	F2	F4	B5	B2	B3	B8	B4	B10
B5	F6	B4	B5	F6	F5	B9	B12	F3	F2
B6	F8	B11	B7	B3	B2	F1	F11	F2	B5
F2	B4	F5	B6	B1	B3	B2	F2	B5	B11
F3	B4	B1	F5	B6	B10	B7	B8	B11	F1
B6	B12	B6	B8	F1	F2	B2	B5	B2	B5
F4	F9	B7	F6	F12	B3	F1	F10	B7	F4

a) Make two tables, one for British and one for Foreign, showing the numbers of cars of each age.

b) Calculate the mean age and the median age of the foreign cars.

c) Draw a histogram to show the ages of British cars, using 0 up to 1, 1 up to 2, ..., 11 up to 12 years as intervals. Why is a histogram suitable for showing this information? Why are the intervals appropriate?

d) It is required to summarize the results of this survey in a table which labels all cars aged 6 years and upwards 'older' and all cars 5 years or less 'newer'. British and foreign cars are to be kept separate in this table.

Design a suitable two-way table, with space for showing 'older' totals and 'newer' totals, British totals and foreign totals. Give your table clear headings and include a footnote to explain 'older' and 'newer'. referring it to the appropriate part of this table.

e) Enter the summary figures in your table and complete all the totals. Make any brief comment on the figures which you think is important.

RSA 1984

3 Pictorial Representation

INTRODUCTION

1 In this Chapter the various means of pictorially displaying data are discussed. The purpose of a picture is discussed as are the general features of the data to be displayed. The three standard categories of picture are covered. These are

Bar Charts
Pie Charts
Line Graphs

There are three major parts to this Chapter. They are;

The Purpose of a Picture
General Features of Data
Pictograms.

THE PURPOSE OF A PICTURE

2 The purpose of a picture is to display the general features and the petterns of the data. A picture is not appropriate for displaying the detail within the numerical data. It has to be realised that a picture is looked at as whole and it is very rare for the casual viewer to closely scrutinise the details. Ordinarily the picture is glanced at sufficiently long for the general impression to be conveyed. For these reasons we must chose a picture that will most effectively display whatever features of the data need to be emphasised.

THE GENERAL FEATURES OF DATA

3 We shall consider three broad categories of features that occur in data. They are;

Relative sizes of data
Proportions of a whole
Changes of data over time

RELATIVE SIZES OF DATA

Women have a greater life expectancy than men.
Men are generally taller than women.
There are more owner occupied than rented houses in Britain.
There are fewer black and white TV sets than colour

4 All these statements concern the relative sizes of data. The most effective way to illustrate measurements of relative size is to use BAR CHARTS.

BAR CHARTS

5 A BAR CHART is a picture consisting of a set of horizontal or vertical bars. The lengths of the bars represent the size of the appropriate data.

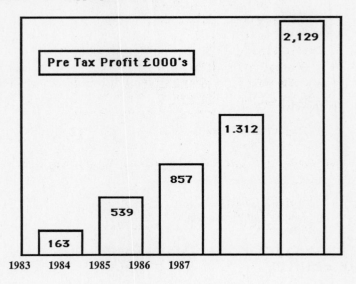

This picture shows clearly the relative sizes of the profits in each successive year. Also included are the profits rounded to the nearest £1000. These figures are there to emphasize the numerical values of the profits. As mentioned earlier, pictures are used to display patterns in data rather than the specific numerical values. If it is desired to indicate the numerical sizes of data in a picture then they must be specifically displayed. Another way of displaying numerical data is to use a scale as is done in the next picture.

6 In the following diagram the bars are arranged horizontally. This particular arrangement was used to allow the different activities to be written alongside each bar. Again, relative sizes are clearly illustrated and this time a scale is included to give the viewer some idea of numerical size. If the specific values had been entered as in the last picture the overall effect would have been too fussy. Simplicity of presentation is essential.

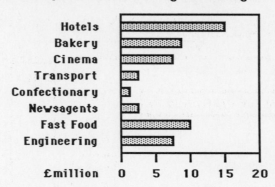

A bar chart can consist of SINGLE BARS as we have just seen. Alternativey we can use

> Multiple Bars
> Back-to-back bars
> Component bars
> Gantt Charts

MULTIPLE BARS

7 A multiple bar chart is a number of single bar charts superimposed on top of each other. The purpose of such a chart is to contrast more than one sequence of data values. The following chart shows the relative percentages of smokers in different age groups and contrasts the differences between men and women.

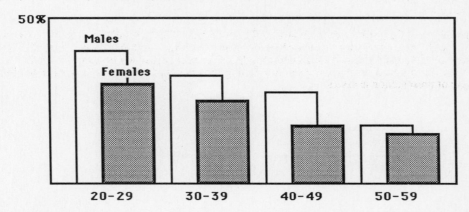

Here the relative percentages of men and women are highlighted by using contrasting shading. The exact numerical values are not given because only the pattern of the data was required to be shown.

In the following picture the bars are arranged horizontally.

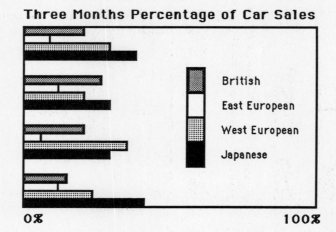

In this picture we can immediately see the changes in the relative sizes of sales of cars with different country of origin. Again, notice the shading to highlight the differences. The key explains the meaning of the shading as an alternative to writing the country of origin against each bar.

BACK-TO-BACK BARS

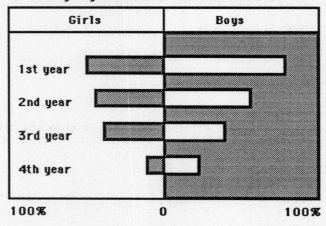

8 Back to back bars illustrate comparisons in much the same way as multiple bars do. Notice the shading. This was done to create a picture that attracted attention. A picture is of little use if no-one looks at it.

COMPONENT BARS

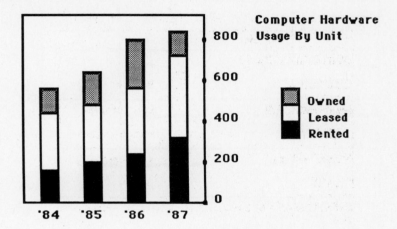

9 Component bars are simply multiple bars laid directly on top of each other. The top line of one component is the base line of the next component. Again, notice the shading to distinguish one set of bars from another.

GANTT CHARTS

10 A GANTT CHART is used to illustrate progress. The following table records the sales enquires and subsequent orders achieved by a company.

Month	Sales Enquiries	Sales Orders	Orders as a %ge of Enquiries	Cumulative Percentage
1	100	60	60%	60%
2	50	20	40%	100%
3	130	117	90%	190%
4	100	36	36%	226%

The Gantt chart is constructed as shown. Each month division is taken to represent 100%. The bar in that month represents the percentage achieved. By building the chart month by month as we have done it is also possible to plot a cumulative achievement as well.

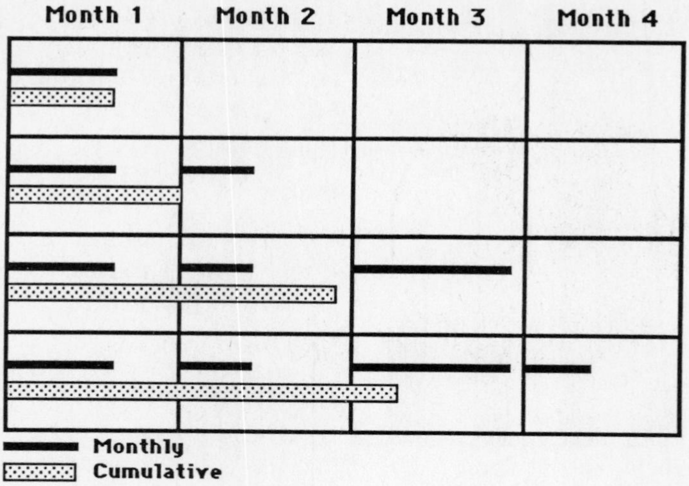

PROPORTIONS OF A WHOLE

In 1977, 10% of all births in the UK occured outside marriage
In 1981, 6% of all 16 - 18 year-olds were on a Youth Opportunities Scheme

11 These statements concern the proportionate sizes of data. The most effective way to illustrate proportional sizes of data is to use PIE CHARTS.

PIE CHARTS

12 A PIE CHART consists of a circle representing the whole with segments marked off representing the proportions. To distinguish the proportions the segments can be shaded. Shading also makes the picture more interesting. Notice the key to explain the shading in the following picture.

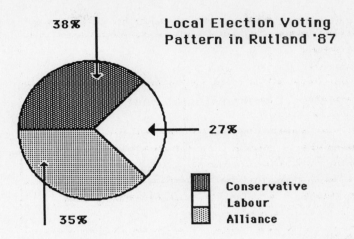

A pie chart can be a SIMPLE pie chart as just shown or we can use;

An exploded pie
A three dimensional pie
Comparative pies

EXPLODED PIE

13 An exploded pie has one or more segments slightly removed as shown in the following picture.

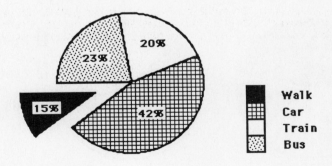

An exploded pie such as this gives dramatic effect. In this pie the proportion of walkers is of particular interest. By exploding the pie in this way the eye is drawn to that particular proportion.

THREE DIMENSIONAL PIES

Proportion of Consumption of Fast Food

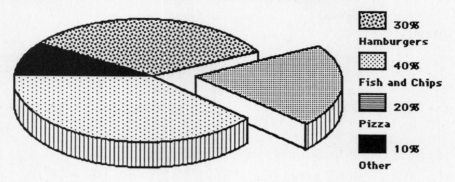

14 Using three dimensions in an exploded pie makes the picture much more eye-catching. Also, in this case, as it is the pizza consumption that is highlighted, the use of a pie adds a special touch.

COMPARATIVE PIES

15 Comparative pies can be used to compare relative proportions at two different times and so illustrate changes in the proportions.

Comparative Uses of Different Fuels

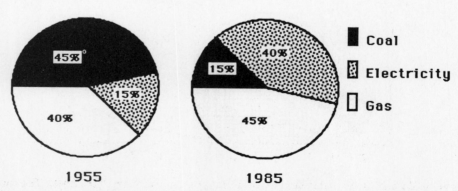

Notice that both pies are the same size. If the population has increased during the two times illustrated there is a temptation to increase the size of the second pie to illustrate this fact. Avoid the temptation. The pies should only be used to compare relative proportions and their changes.

CHANGES IN DATA OVER TIME

Between 1961 and 1981 the relative price index of domestic gas fell steadily whereas that of domestic electricity remained the same.
Consumer spending on personal telephones has steadily risen over the past twenty years.

16 These statements concern the changes in data over time. The most effective way to illustrate changes in data over time is to use the LINE GRAPH

LINE GRAPHS

17 We have already extensively discussed single line graphs, including multiple lines and layered graphs, in Chapter 6 of Section 3. The only line graph we shall consider here is the Z CHART.
Z-CHARTS

18 The following table records purchases made by a company over a year. The record consists of each months ppurchases, that month's moving annual total and that month's cumulative total.

Purchases £(00's)

	J	F	M	A	M	J	J	A	S	O	N	D
Current	20	30	10	15	25	20	10	5	10	15	20	35
Moving Total	195	200	220	210	200	190	200	210	200	220	210	215
Cumulative	20	50	60	75	100	120	130	135	145	160	180	215

We now plot each of these three records on the same graph.

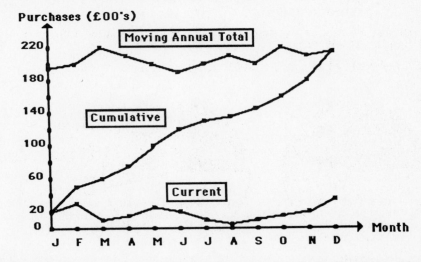

This is the Z CHART, so called because of the letter Z formed by the three lines. The current line illustrates the month by month purchases showing any seasonal variations that may exist. The moving annual total shows the annual purchases with the seasonal variations taken out - it is the TREND line. The cumulative line shows the accumulated purchases month by month.

PICTOGRAMS

19 Pictograms are artistically embellished versions of the various types of pictures that we have already considered. The following two examples have appeared in the press.

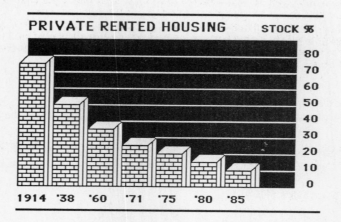

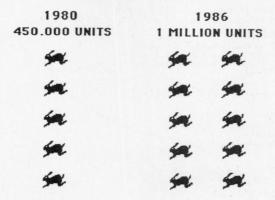

20 Well constructed pictograms are excellent eye-catchers. They can be used to great effect when trying to illustrate data patterns to the casual reader. Pictograms are many and varied being restricted only by the imagination of their creators. Look around and you will see them everywhere.

SUMMARY

21 The purpose of a picture is to display the general features of data. Consequently, the feature to be displayed will determine the type of picture used. If we wish to display the relative sizes of data we would use a bar chart. If we want to illustrate relative proportions then a pie chart is ideal. Changes of data over time are best illustrated using a line graph. Within each category of picture there are a number of choices. And again, the choice will be determined by the data. Whichever picture is chosen it must be simple and uncluttered otherwise the feature being displayed could be lost in detail. When constructing a picture our imagination is our only restriction. Pictograms can be designed to both convey the necessary message and to catch the eye of the casual reader.

KEY POINTS TO NOTE

22 Bar charts, Pie charts, Line graphs, Pictograms, Relative sizes of data, Proportions of a whole, Changes in data over time

STUDENT SELF TESTING

SELF REVIEW QUESTIONS

1. List four categories of picture. (1)

2. What is the purpose of a picture? (2)

3. List three general features of data that can be displayed by a picture. (3)

4. What sort of data are bar charts best suited for? (4)

5. List five types of bar chart. (5)

6. What sort of data are pie charts best suited for? (11)

7. Describe a pie chart. (12)

8. List four type of pie chart. (12)

9. What sort of data are line graphs best suited for? (16)

10. Describe the contents of a Z-chart. (18)

EXERCISES (Answers begin on Page 249)

1. Describe the important features and the principle uses of any TWO of the following statistical diagrams. Give a diagrammatic example to illustrate each of your answers.

a) Pie Diagram

b) Cumulative Frequency Graph

c) Pictogram

d) Histogram

LCCI 1985

2. The following table shows the population of England and Wales, in thousands, in various age-groups for the years 1951, 1961, 1971, 1981.

Age Group	1951	1961	1971	1981
Under 5	3718	3597	3905	2910
5 - 14	5974	6987	7671	7053
15 - 29	8912	8925	10236	10859
30 - 44	9767	9263	8593	9541
45 - 64	10563	11836	11849	10884
65 - 74	3257	3520	4178	4488
75 and over	1568	1976	2318	2786

Source: *Office of Population Censuses and Statistics*

a) Draw component bar charts to illustrate the 1951 and 1981 figures.

b) Draw a horizontal multiple bar chart to illustrate each year's figures.

RSA 1985

3. Describe the important features and the principle uses of any TWO of the following statistical diagrams. Give a diagrammatic example to illustrate each of your answers.

a) Scattergraph

b) Bar Charts

c) Lorentz Curve

d) Z Chart

LCCI 1984

4. A chain store collected the following bata from three branches.

Sales (£000's) Branches	1984	Year 1985	1986	1987
Birmingham	25	40	52	60
Leeds	30	35	50	55
Glasgow	25	34	49	52
TOTAL	83	109	151	167

Illustrate each branch's data using

a) Multiple Line Graphs

b) Comparative Pie Charts

c) Multiple vertical bar charts.

4 The Use Of Words

INTRODUCTION

1 In this Chapter we consider the use of words for presenting the conclusions of a Statistical Enquiry.

There are three major parts to this Chapter. They are;

> **The Purpose of Words**
> **Summarizing a Table or Picture**
> **Summarizing The Conclusions as a Whole**

THE PURPOSE OF WORDS

2 Words are an essential component in the presentation of conclusions drawn from a statistical enquiry. Their purpose is twofold;

> **Summarizing a Table or Picture**
> **Summarizing the Conclusions as a Whole**

SUMMARIZING A TABLE OR PICTURE

3 Every table and picture conveys a message but that message is incomplete without without a short written summary. This summary should point out the patterns or other important features displayed in the table or picture. The summary and the table or picture should be adjacent to each other. This gives the appearance of a complete display unit and encourages the reader to read the summary. The summary should be brief and should not refer to anything that is not portrayed in the table or picture.

SUMMARIZING THE CONCLUSIONS AS A WHOLE

4 When all the demonstration tables have been completed and all the charts, diagrams and graphs have been drawn the final summary of the conclusions as a whole must be written. It is at this stage that all the previous work done is gathered together and presented to the reader. To avoid wasting all the earlier effort of collecting and analysing the data this written summary must be effective. To ensure that it is so it is best structured in two parts.

> **The Conclusions**
> **The Source**

THE CONCLUSIONS

5 Start the report with the conclusions. If possible list them under a separate heading. Do not succumb to excessive reporting. Highlight two or three major findings at most.

THE SOURCES

6 Describe the source of the data and how it was obtained. State any conditions that were imposed on the source and comment on any effect that these conditions might have had on the conclusions.

7 In writing the report try to adopt a crisp style. Keep the sentences short. When you find them becoming too long, re-phrase your ideas. In this way one long sentence may be split into two or three others. Avoid all jargon or technical terms. Use only familiar words. Be precise in your use of the language. Do not sensationalise by using emotive words. If a number is large, do not describe it as huge. Avoid bias in all your writing. Above all be objective. When presenting your findings your opinions are irrelevant. The only aspect that matters is that the conclusions as found are conveyed to the reader.

SUMMARY

8 Words are essential in the presentation of the results of a statistical enquiry. They are used to summarise tables and pictures. They are also used to present the final summary of the conclusions as a whole. In all situations the prose should be clear and precise. The language used should be familiar and to the point. The message conveyed must be devoid of any bias or opinion and should present the conclusions objectively.

KEY POINTS TO NOTE

9 Words, Summarizing a table, Summarizing the conclusions as a whole

STUDENT SELF TESTING

SELF REVIEW QUESTIONS

1. What are two uses of words when presenting the results of a statistical enquiry? (2)

2. What features should a table or picture summary possess? (3)

3. How should the summary of the conclusions as a whole be structured? (4-6)

EXERCISES (Answers begin on Page 249)

1. From the following diagram;

a) Draw up a table showing the percentages of males and of females in each socio-economic group that do not wear glasses.

b) Show using pie charts, the proportions of ALL males and ALL females in the four classifications described in the diagram.

In each case read off figures as accurately as you can from the diagram.

Write a brief report on what the diagram tells you

Why do you think footnote * is included?

Eyesight Difficulty*: by sex and socio-economic group. 1981

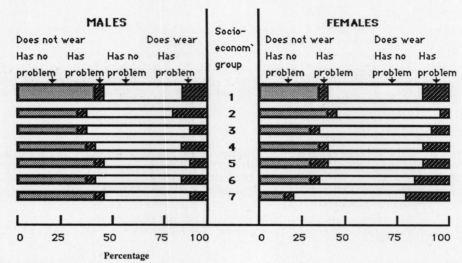

Percentage

* For persons 16 and over

Socio-economic groups

1. All
2. Professional
3. Employers and Managers
4. Intermediate and junior non-manual
5. Skilled manual and own account non-professional
6. Semi-skilled manual and personal service
7. Unskilled manual

RSA 1984

Appendix   Further Probability

INTRODUCTION

1 In this appendix we consider probabilities of outcomes to a random experiment that are connected by AND and OR. We define a random experiment and devise a notation for the probabilities of the outcomes. The complement of an outcome is defined as is its probability.

RANDOM EXPERIMENT

2 A RANDOM EXPERIMENT is the name given to any experiment that has a number of possible outcomes. For example,

1. Tossing a coin is an EXPERIMENT. It is a RANDOM EXPERIMENT because the result of the experiment has TWO POSSIBLE outcomes - a head or a tail.

2. Let a drawer contain three socks, a red one, a blue one and a white one. Selecting a sock blindfold is an EXPERIMENT. It is a RANDOM EXPERIMENT because the result of the experiment has THREE POSSIBLE outcomes - the selection of red sock, a blue sock or a white sock.

NOTATION

3 In a random experiment every possible outcome has a PROBABILITY associated with it. The probability of a tossed coin coming up heads is 1/2. The probability of selecting a blue sock out of our drawer is 1/3. We shall use the notation

Pr(outcome)

to represent the PROBABILITY OF AN OUTCOME. So that,

Pr(a head)   = 1/2
Pr(a tail)   = 1/2
Pr(a blue sock) = 1/3

THE SUM OF ALL PROBABILITIES

4 The sum of all the probabilites associated with outcomes of a random experiment equals 1. For example,

Pr(a head) + Pr(a tail) = 1/2 + 1/2

= 1

241

Pr(ablue sock) + Pr(a red sock) + Pr(a white sock)

$$= 1/3 + 1/3 + 1/3$$

$$= 1$$

THE COMPLEMENT OF AN OUTCOME

5 The COMPLEMENT of an outcome occuring is the outcome NOT OCCURING. Since any particular outcome either occurs or it does not occur,

Pr(outcome) + Pr(not outcome) = 1

For example,

Pr(a blue sock) $= 1/3$

Pr(not a blue sock) $= 1 - 1/3$

$$= 2/3$$

EXAMPLE

6 The following table shows the number of male and female staff in each of three sections of an electronics company.

	Production	Administration	Sales
Male	27	9	34
Female	28	11	11

An employee is selected at random. Calculate the probability that the employee is

a) Male
b) Not a production worker
c) A female production worker
d) Not a female salesperson

LCCI 1985

SOLUTION

7 By addition there are 70 male workers and 50 female workers making 120 workers in total. By using these numbers and the number in the table we can easily dedude that;

a) Pr(a male) = 70/120

b) Pr(not a production worker)
$= 1 - $ Pr(a production worker)
$= 1 - 55/120$
$= 65/120$

c) Pr(a female production worker)
       = 28/120

d) Pr(not a female sales person)
           = 1 - Pr(a female sales person)
           = 1 - 11/120
           = 109/120

MUTUALLY EXCLUSIVE OUTCOMES

8 If we select a sock out of our drawer and we find that it is blue then it is not red and it is not white. The selection of a blue sock and the selection of a red sock are MUTUALLY EXCLUSIVE OUTCOMES. If the occurrence of outcome 1 means that outcome 2 has not occurred and vice versa then outcomes 1 and 2 are MUTUALLY EXCLUSIVE - the occurrence of either outcome EXCLUDES the possibility of the other outcome occurring.

THE CONNECTION 'OR'

9 Outcomes to a random experiment can be CONNECTED by OR.

outcome 1 OR outcome 2

means

EITHER outcome 1 occurs
OR   outcome 2 occurs

If two outcomes are mutually exclusive, then

Pr(outcome 1 OR outcome 2)

= Pr(outcome1) + Pr(outcome 2)

For example,
           Pr(a red sock OR a white sock)

= Pr(a red sock) + Pr(a white sock)

= 2/3

DEPENDENT OUTCOMES

10 If two random experiments are performed one after the other then it may be possible for the outcome of the first experiment to affect the outcome of the second. If this is the case the outcomes are DEPENDENT upon each other. Let

Experiment 1 be selecting a sock out of our drawer
Experiment 2 be selecting another sock out of our drawer

Let the outcome of experiment 1 be the selection of a blue sock with probability 1/3. This now affects the probabilities for our second selection as there are only TWO socks left in the drawer. For experiment 2

$$\text{Pr(a red sock)} \qquad = 1/2$$

$$\text{Pr(a white sock)} \qquad = 1/2$$

$$\text{Pr(a blue sock)} \qquad = 0$$

This last probability is zero as there are no blue socks in the drawer after the first selection. This outcome is IMPOSSIBLE.

INDEPENDENT OUTCOMES

11 If the outcome of the first experiment does not affect the outcome of the second experiment then the outcomes are INDEPENDENT of each other. If we had replaced the blue sock before experiment 2 then we should have had INDEPENDENT OUTCOMES. There would have been three socks in the drawere ready for experiment 2 with

$$\text{Pr(a red sock)} \qquad = 1/3$$

$$\text{Pr(a white sock)} \qquad = 1/3$$

$$\text{Pr(a blue sock)} \qquad = 1/3$$

THE CONNECTION 'AND'

12 Outcomes from successive random experiments can be connected by AND.

$$\text{outcome 1 AND outcome 2}$$

means

$$\text{BOTH outcome 1 occurs}$$
$$\text{AND outcome 2 occurs}$$

If the two outcomes are INDEPENDENT then

$$\text{Pr(outcome 1 AND outcome 2)}$$

$$= \text{Pr(outcome 1) x Pr(outcome 2)}$$

For example, the probability of obtaining a tail from tossing a coin and drawing a white sock out of our drawer is

$$\text{Pr(a tail AND a white sock)}$$

$$= \text{Pr(a tail) x Pr(a white sock)}$$

$$= (1/2) \text{ x } (1/3)$$

$$= 1/6$$

EXAMPLE

13 In a factory, items pass through two processes, namely pressing and finishing. The probability that an item has a pressing fault is 0.1 and the probability that an item has a finishing fault is 0.2. Pressing and finishing faults occur independently of one another. Calculate the probabilty that a selected item

a) Has both pressing and finishing faults
b) Has neither pressing nor finishing faults
c) Has a pressing fault but does not have a finishing fault

LCCI 1986

SOLUTION

14 Pressing and Finishing are independent of each other. Let

Pressing be experiment 1
Finishing be experiment 2

In experiment 1

We are given: Pr(pressing fault)   = 0.1

hence   Pr(not pressing fault)   = 0.9
since any item either does or does not have a pressing fault

In experiment 2

We are given: Pr(finishing fault)   = 0.2
hence   Pr(not finishing fault)   = 0.8

a) Pr(pressing fault AND finishing fault)

= Pr(pressing fault) x Pr(finishing fault)

=(0.1) x (0.2)

=0.02

b) Pr(no pressing fault AND no finishing fault)

= Pr(no pressing fault) x Pr(no finishing fault

= (0.9) x (0.8)

= 0.72

c) Pr(pressing fault AND no finishing fault)

$$= \text{Pr(pressing fault)} \times \text{Pr(no finishing fault)}$$

$$= (0.1) \times (0.8)$$

$$= 0.08$$

SUMMARY

15 The possible outcomes of random experiments have probabilities associated with them. The probability of a particular outcome occurring added to the probability of it not occurring equals unity. Several outcomes from a single experiment can be connected by OR. If two outcomes of a single random experiment are mutually exclusive, the probability of one OR the other occurring is equal to the SUM of the respective probabilties of each occurring.

An outcome of one experiment can be connected to an outcome of a second experiment by AND. If two such outcomes are INDEPENDENT then the probability of the first occurring AND the second occurring is equal to the product of the respective probabilities of each occurring.

KEY POINTS TO NOTE

16 Random experiment, Outcomes, Pr(outcome), Complement, NOT, Mutually exclusive, OR, Dependent uotcomes, Independent outcomes, AND

STUDENT SELF TESTING

SELF REVIEW QUESTIONS

1. What is a random experiment? (2)

2. What is the complement of an outcome occurring? (5)

3. What is meant by the phrase "outcome 1 and outcome 2 are mutually exclusive"? (8)

4. How do we calculate the probability of two mutually exclusive oucomes connected by OR? (9)

5. What are independent outcomes? (11)

6. How do we calculate the probability of two independent outcomes occurring connected by AND? (12)

EXERCISES (Answers begin on Page 249)

1. A box contains lead pencils of three different grades, B, HB and H. The pencils are painted either brown or yellow. The following table shows the quantity of each in the box.

	B	HB	H
Brown	20	15	5
Yellow	25	20	15

A pencil is selected at random. Calculate the probability that it is;

a) painted yellow
b) Not a B grade
c) A brown HB
d) Not a yellow H
e) Either a brown HB or a red B

2. From a deck of 52 playing cards one card is selected at random. What are the probabilities that the card is;

a) An ACE?
b) A red card?
c) The JACK of CLUBS?
d) Not a black SEVEN?
e) A red FOUR or a black TWO?
f) The QUEEN of DIAMONDS or the ACE of HEARTS?

3. A lamp is taken at random from a production line and tested. If the bulb does not light up two possible causes of the fault could be either a faulty switch or a faulty bulb. The switch is likely to be faulty with a probability of 0.1 and the bulb is likely to be faulty with a probability of 0.3. Switch and bulb faults are independent of each other.

Calculate the probability that a defective lamp

a) has both a switch fault and a bulb fault
b) has neither a switch fault not a bulb fault
c) has a switch fault but does not have a bulb fault
d) has either a switch fault or a bulb fault

4. If the card in Question 1 is replaced in the deck, the deck shuffled and a second card drawn, what are the probabilities that;

a) Both cards were an ACE?
b) Both cards were red?
c) The first card was not a FOUR and the second was not a TWO?
d) At least one of the two cards was a KING?
e) Would your answers be different if the first card had not been replaced?

Answers To Exercises

The answers to the even numbered exercises that appear at the end of each Chapter are given here.

Section 1

Chapter 1

2. Week 6 is the longest, week 5 is the shortest. Total is 44.

This problem demonstrates that the answer can sometimes be derived from a simple inspection of the data and sometimes from a simple manipulation of the data.

Chapter 2

2. To which households does the question refer? Does the word **borrow** include books read in the library as well as those taken home? Over what period of time is the question considering, a week, a month or a year?

How many books do [*households*] borrow from the Public Library in a [*period*]

The **households** and the **period** must be defined to properly pose the question.

Chapter 3

2. How often do people visit the cinema?

To construct a questionnaire to collect the required data we must

a) Identify the people we are going to ask. We must be very careful that we do not collect data from a specific group of people and then assume that the results found from their replies apply to *all* people.

b) Decide when the questionnair is to be distributed and the last date for its return. We must establish the *management* processes involved in handling the questionnaire.
Having done this we must design the questionnaire form. This will consist of an introductory section explaining who is requesting the information and to what purposes it is to be put,

The next section will contain the question. This question must be phrased in such a way that it allows the most accurate responses possible. There is a large number of possible replies to this question. The main task is to reduce the possible replies to a manageable amount. We use the following reasoning;

a) Some people NEVER go to the cinema.

b) Some people do go but only very occasionally. These people may not be able to specify exactly how often they visit the cinema.

c) Some people are regular visitors. We must cater for these.

d) Finally, we must allow for 'other' responses. Our reasoning may not have considered all the possibilites. Inserting an 'other' response should help to cater for this.

How often do you visit the cinema?

Never	☐
Occasionally	☐
Once a week	☐
Once a month	☐
Other (Please specify)	_____

The final section will consist of instructions regarding the completion of the questionnaire and how it is to be returned.

Chapter 4

2. a) By crossing off numbers as shown it is possible to make an accurate count. After the frequencies have been counted the frequencies themselves should be counted. This provides a check that the frequencies were counted correctly.

Scores on 60 Rolls

Number	Frequency
1	15
2	9
3	9
4	9
5	9
6	9

```
1 2 6 1 4 3 6 4 1 6
1 1 5 6 5 1 5 2 5 2
4 3 1 3 1 4 3 5 6 4
1 6 4 4 2 6 2 4 1 5
2 1 3 1 5 1 2 6 3 2
3 6 1 5 2 4 5 6 1 3
```

b) Multiplying each score by its frequency and then adding yields the total score for the 60 rolls to be 195. Dividing by the number of rolls yields the **average** score.

$$(1 \times 15 + 2 \times 9 + 3 \times 9 + 4 \times 9 + 5 \times 9 + 6 \times 9) \div 60 = 195 \div 60$$

$$= 3.25$$

c) According to the 60 rolls it would appear that the die is not fair because the number 1 appears substantially more times than any other. However, if the die were rolled a further 30 times and the numbers 2, 3, 4, 5 and 6 came up 6 times each then we would feel entitled to conclude that the die *was* fair.

Chapter 5

2. To create the required table we must first construct some preliminary tables. We do this by reading the question a bit at a time. Firstly, we tabulate the different types of fault.

FAULTS			
Stuctural	Plumbing	Electrical	Other
400	300	700	600

The number 400, 300, 700 come direclty from the question. The number 600 is deduced from the fact that the total number of faults is 2000. Thus

$$2000 - (400 + 300 + 700) = 600$$

Secondly, we tabulate the type of building that the faults related to.

FAULTS		
Flats	Bungalows	Houses
800	500	700

The numbers 800 and 500 come directly from the question. The number 700 is deduced by subtracting the 800 and 500 from 2000, the total number of faults. Thirdly, we tabulate the type of building that *specific* faults related to,

251

STRUCTURAL		
Flats	Bungalows	Houses
200	100	100

Of the 400 structural faults half (200) related to Flats, one quarter (100) related to houses.

PLUMBING		
Flats	Bungalows	Houses
100	50	150

Of the 300 plumbing faults, half (150) related to houses and a third (100) to Flats.

ELECTRICAL.		
Flats	Bungalows	Houses
350	175	175

Of the 700 electrical faults a quarter (175) related to houses and a quarter (175) related to bungalows.

Finally, we draw these five tables together into one single table.

FAULTS RECORDED IN NEW BUILDINGS

	Structural	Plumbing	Electrical	Other	TOTAL
Flats	200	100	350	150	800
Bungalows	100	50	175	175	500
Houses	100	150	175	275	700
TOTAL	400	300	700	600	2000

The first, second, third and fifth column of numbers are obtained from the earlier tables. The column headed **Other** is obtained by sutracting the first three columns from the fifth. For example, There are 800 faults recorded in the Flats, of which 200 are structural, 100 plumbing and 350 electrical. Consequently, there must be

$$800 - (200 + 100 + 350) = 150$$

other faults. The TOTALS are given as a check on the consistency of the recorded data.

The purpose of this question is to demonstrate how a large amount of written information can be reduced to tabulated numbers by taking the written information a bit at a time. Many problems are like jigsaws - the final picture emerges by building up sections and then joining the sections together.

b) The distribution of the faults over all types of building is displayed in the following pictogram.

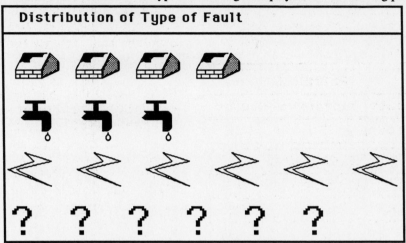

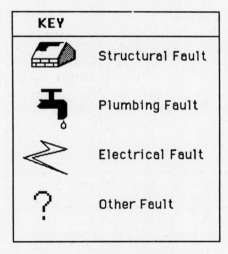

Each symbol represents **100** Faults.

Section 2

Chapter 1

2. To build the bridge the Company must borrow money from the bank. To repay this money and any interest charged on the loan the Company will earn income by levying a toll on the users of the bridge.

Question

1. How much money does the Company need to borrow from the bank to undertake a successful completion of the bridge?

Assume that by the time the bridge opens and the Company starts to earn income the Company owes the bank an amount £AMOUNT_1. Assume also that the Company has an arrangement to repay its debt over a ten year period and that in doing so the total amount paid back will be £AMOUNT_2. (£AMOUNT_2 includes £AMOUNT_1 plus any interest paid during the 10 year period). Ths Company must now ensure that their income after expenses and tax over the ten year period is greater than £AMOUNT_2.

2. How many different forms of transport will use the bridge? For example, pedestrians, cyclists, motorists etc.

3. How many of each different form of transport will use the bridge?

4. How much toll can be levied on each form of transport without discouraging the use of the bridge?

5. How much income will this generate each year for the next ten years?

6. Will this be sufficient to allow the debt to be repaid.

The purpose of this question is not to provide an exhaustive list of questions that arise during the complicated process of building a bridge. The purpose is to demonstrate that serious questions do arise that must be answered and that the only way to answer them is to use a statistical approach. For example, how does anybody predict the use of a bridge over a ten year period in the future? Especially when the bridge does not yet exist. The answer has to be sought via Statistics.

Chapter 2

2. Your five areas of concern are;

> **Production**
> **Stock Control**
> **Manpower**
> **Finance**
> **Sales and Advertising**

Production

Is the Company fully equipped to maintain the current production levels? Does the Company require additional equipment? Is there any redundant equipment that is taking valuable space? Are the premises capable of coping with any increase in production if demand increases?

Stock Control

Is the Company maintaining sufficient stock of raw materials to allow production to proceed without delays? Is there too much stock for the Company's current production level? Can stock levels be decreased to save money being tied up in materials? Are the deliveries on time?

Manpower

Are there enough people to maintain the current production level? Are there too many people for the current production needs? Is there any discontent that is likely to cause production problems? Is the workforce sufficiently skilled to adapt to new techniques? Is it best to hire trainees or ready skilled people?

Finance

Is the Company in debt? To what extent does the Company have to pay suppliers of raw materials before the Company is paid for the finished article? Is the Company's income sufficient to cover operating expenses? How can the manufacturing and management processes be improved so as to increase the level of profit? Should selling prices be reduced to encourage an increase in demand? Should selling prices be increased to take advantage of the products' popularity?

Sales and Advertising

Is the Company selling the finished goods fast enough? Is the sales team capable of coping with an increase in demand? Should the products be advertised more widely? Who buys the Comany's products? Should the Company go to the customer or should it wait for the customer to come to the Company? Is there a need to improve the products presentation to the customer?

This list of questions is not intended to be exhaustive. The purpose of the question is to illustrate the fact that questions must be continually asked to ensure that the necessary information is at hand.

Chapter 3

2. a) **How many doors do you have in your home?**

Number _____

(A door is taken to be a walk-through door only and does not include such doors as cupboard doors)

b) **Do you cycle to work?**

Never   Occasionally   Often   Always

☐   ☐   ☐   ☐

Please tick the appropriate box.

c) **How do you rate your golfing skills?**

      1 2 3 4 5 6 7 8 9 10
      □ □ □ □ □ □ □ □ □ □
   Very Bad   **Very Good**

Please indicate at the appropriate point on the scale

d) **Do you enjoy hiking?**   □ **Yes** □ **No**

Please tick the appropriate box

e) **What are your views on pollution from car exhaust fumes?**

_____
_____
_____

(An open-ended answer is requested in this case)

Chapter 4

2. How much PAYE do you pay in a week?

Flaws:

a) Not everyone can be expected know what PAYE means. It means Pay As You Earn and refers to the income tax paid on income that is earned at regular intevals such as a week or a month. The question has made use of abbreviations without definig what they mean.

b) If the respondant earns a varying amount each week then it will not be possible to give a precise answer to this question. Also, if the respondant is paid monthly there may be some confusion over the number of weeks in a pay-month. Sometimes it may be four and other times it may be five. The question is inccapable of being answered precisely.

One possible re-phrasing is as follows;

How much income tax do you pay each week?

        None   □
        £10 or less   □
        £25 or less but more than £10 □
        More than £25   □

Please tick the appropriate box.

Notice that the information gained from the question only has a certain level of accuracy bit if this is the level of accuracy required then the question is now capable of being answered to that level of accuracy.

4 How much alcohol do you drink in a week?

Flaws:

a) Does the question mean the actual amount of alcohol as a proportion of alcoholic drinks consumed or does it just mean the amount of alcoholic drinks consumed in a week? The question is ambiguous.

b) How many people know how much alcohol there is in the different alcoholic drinks that they consume? The question cannot be precisely answered.

c) How many people keep a record of the alcoholic drinks that they consume? The question relies too much on memory.

The question can be re-phrased as follows;

How much beer do you drink in a week?

None	☐
1 pint or less	☐
2 pints or less but more than 1	☐
More than 2 points	☐

How much wine do you drink in a week?

None	☐
1 bottle or less	☐
2 bottles or less but more than 1	☐
More than 2 bottles	☐

How much alcoholic spirit do you drink in a week?

None	☐
1/2 bottle or less	☐
1 bottle or less but more than 1/2	☐
More than 1 bottle	☐

Please tick the appropriate boxes.

This question quantifies the amount of alcohol by recognising three different types of drink with different levels of alcohol content. It also distinguishes the occasional drinker from the total abstainer by providing the 'None' category.

6. How much exercise do you take in a week?

Flaws:

a) The question does not define 'exercise'. Is the occasional casual stroll to be included as exercise as well as training for a marathon? The question is ambiguous.

b) How much is much? The question is incapable of being precisely answered. Even if the respondant answered YES to this question the questionner would still not know how much exercise was taken.

257

An alternative re-phrasing is as follows;

Do you walk for at least half an hour

At least once a day		☐
At least once a week		☐
Occasionally		☐
Never		☐

Do you run at least one quarter of a mile

At least once a day		☐
At least once a week		☐
Occasionally		☐
Never		☐

Do you participate in a sporting activity

At least once a day		☐
At least once a week		☐
Occasionally		☐
Never		☐

Please tick the appropriate boxes.

This question now distinguishes between different types of activity and sets a measure on each.

Chapter 5

SupaShops PLC
High Street   **9th March**
West Easton

STAFF QUESTIONNAIRE

This questionnaire is being distributed to all employees of SupShops in High Easton to find out by what means employees travel to work and how long it takes them.

It would be greatly appreciated if these questionnaires could be completed as soon as possible and no later than 4.00 pm Friday 13th.

When you have completed your questionnaire please hand it to your supervisor.

There is no need for you to put your name on this questionnaire. Enter your works code number and you will then be identiable to management via your personal file.

CODE _____

1 At what time do you leave home for work _____ am

2 At what time do you arrive at work   _____ am

3 Do you Travel to work by car

☐ No   ☐ Yes

    3a Who drives   Self ☐

                    Another person ☐

4 Do you travel to work by bus

☐ No   ☐ Yes

    4a How long does it take you
        to walk to the bus stop   _____ mins

    4b How many buses do you use

        1 bus   ☐
        2 buses   ☐
        More than 2 buses. Specify _____

    4c What is your total
        waiting time   _____ mins

5 Do you travel to work by train

☐ No   ☐ Yes

5a How long does it take you
    to walk to the station   _____ mins

5b Which train service do you use

☐ Northern Line
☐ Southern Line
☐ Western Line
☐ Eastern Line

Please tick the appropriate box

Chapter 6

2 The people questioned could be sensitive to the queries if they were personally affected by the adverse weather. If, for example, they had direct experience of an elderly person dying from hypothermia brought on by insufficient heating then they are more likely to react emotionally than to react in a considered manner. Such a person could over-emphasise their normal opinions of how much they expect Government to be responsible for the welfare of the population.

On the positive side the prevailing conditions would mean that some time could have been spent thinking about the issue. As a result the respondant is less likely to give an off hand, casual response.

Section 3

Chapter 1

2. The interview method of collecting primary data allows a respondant to be asked questions on a person to person basis. There are two methods of executing the interview and these are;

Direct Interview
Indirect Interview

DIRECT INTERVIEW

In the direct interview the questionner and the respondant face each other. The success of the interview will depend upon the skill and personality of the interviewer. Amongst the various skills the interviewer must posses are the ability to manage people, the ability to listen and the abiltiy to put the respondant at ease. The interviewer must be able to pesuade the respondant to answer the questions. To some people these skills come naturally, others have to acquire them through formal training courses.

The interviewer must be lively and give the impression of interest in the answers to the questions even if the respondant is the hundredth person they have interviewed that day.

The interviewer must be tactful. The interviewer must neither offend nor generate hostility in the person being interviewed. Otherwise the answers will reflect that immediate hostility rather than the considered opinion.

The interviewer's feeling about the questions must not be allowed to colour the respondants feelings thereby affecting the answers.

Keep it cheerful. If there is no fun there will be little point and it will be difficult to maintain the interest of the person being interviewed.

The phrasing of questions must be accurate and the answers must be accurately acquired and accurately recorded.

INDIRECT INTERVIEW

The indirect interview could be by telephone where the interviewer and the person being interviewed are remote from one another. In this situation the interviewer must establish his or her skills without the benefit of eye contact. Because of this additional skills are required.

The interviewers manner must be pleasing and cheerful even in the face of hostility. At all times the interviewer must be polite.

The interviewer should ensure that he or she speaks clearly and distincly. The questions should be particularly short.

Keep the entire interview as short as possible otherwise the respondant may lose interest.

4. Primary data is data that is collected first hand - at source. There are a number of ways of collecting primary data one of which is through a Diary.

A diary is a record of all the events that happen to a group of people in relation to some specific facet of life. For example, The Family Expenditure Survey and the Viewing Diary in the USA. In the Family Expenditure Survey a number of families each keep a diary of their expediture over a given period. In the Viewing Diary a selection of household record their television viewing. This is of assistance to the various television Companies when planning their future programmes. In the USA a large number of the television programmes are sponsored by specific advertisers. In order to convince the advertisers that there will be sufficient viewers to see their commercials the television companies use the results of the Viewing Diaries.

The advantage of a diary is that a complete record of a group of people can be obtained thereby allowing very accurate data to be obtained.

The disadvantage of a diary is that it does require to be completely filled in at regular intervals. This places a responsibilitry on the keeper of the diary that may not be fulfilled.

Chapter 2

2. a) A random sample is chosen from the workforce on the principle that every member of the workforce has an equal chance of being selected. To enable this each member of the workforce must be identified with a unique number between 1 and 400. Having done this 8 numbers are then selected at random from the 400. These 8 numbers will then identify the people who are to form the committee. To create a PERFECT random sample each member of the workforce must have the same probability **1/400** of being chosen. In practice this would not be possible. For example suppose that the first number chosen was **123** then this number would be removed from the list of numbers leaving **399** from which to chose the second number, this time with a probability of **1/399** and not **1/400**. In order to retain the same probability of **1/400** for every selection then any number selected must stay in the list. This could possibly result in the same person being selected all eight times which would produce a committe of **1**. There are a number of ways of making the random selection.

The numbers 1 to 400 could be written on separate slips of paper, the papers put into a box and thoroughly jumbled up. The 8 numbers could then be selected at random from the box.

A computer program could be written that would generate a set of eight random numbers between 1 and 400.

A set of random number tables could be used. Random number table consist of computer generated tables of 3 digit numbers. By selecting numbers at random from these tables the first 8 three digit numbers less than or equal to 400 could then be used to identify the committee members. This method of selection may produce a committee that is not representative of the workforce For example, the entire committee could possibly be selected from a single department.

b) In a stratified sample the random selection takes place within defined strata. In this situation the defined strata could very well be the four different departments. The two departments having **100** people each form on quarter of the workforce and as a result should contribute one quarter of the committee. That is **2** people each. These two people are then selected randomly from each of these two departments. The remaining two departments have **80** and **120** people respectively and could contribute **1** and **3** committee members each, again these people being selected randomly. This means that the representation of each department is not exactly proportional to the number of people in the department but the representation could be better than that produced by a random sample.

c) In a quota sample the 8 committee members form the quota. The actual members could then be selected quite arbitrarily. Provided **8** people are selected the quota is achieved.

4. a) RANDOM SAMPLING. Each pupil is identified by a unique number. 50 numbers are then selected at random by using random number tables. This creates a random sample of 50 pupils.

b) CLUSTER SAMPLING. Every person to be questioned is selected according to a specific characteristic, namely, over the age of 40.

c) STRATIFIED SAMPLING or QUOTA SAMPLING. The two strata are defined as peolpe under the age of 18 and people over the age of 65. If within each strata the people to be interviewed are selected at random by using random selection techniques the sample so formed will be a stratified sample. If. however, within the strata the people to be interviewed are selected without using random selection techniques the sample will be a quota sample. For example, the people chosen could be from those people in the town market on a particular day.

Chapter 3

2. Ranked Bonuses : 9.96 11.69 12.74 12.98 13.76 14.64 14.73 16.93 17.54 17.68 22.43

This question tests a knowledge of the word **RANK** and the ability to manipulate a confusion of numbers.

4.

Number	Frequency
1	8
2	7
3	6
4	8
5	6
6	5
7	4
8	4
9	2
TOTAL	**50**

4 8 6 5 3 2 1 9 4 1
3 5 2 8 7 2 2 3 5 1
7 5 7 4 1 5 6 8 4 5
6 1 3 1 6 4 2 1 8 7
2 4 6 4 3 1 2 9 3 4

By drawing a line through the numbers as they are counted a check of those numbers counted is made.

A count is made of the frequencies as a check that the frequencies have been counted correctly.

Chapter 4

2

Football Team Goal Record

	Games Played									TOTAL
	1	2	3	4	5	6	7	8	9	
Goals Scored	2	1	3	0	0	1	0	2	0	9

4. To produce a table that summarizes the data in this question we must first construct a number of preliminary tables. To do this we consider the information given in the question in steps. The information given concerns

Grade of hotel
Location of all hotels
Location of luxury hotels
Location of superior hotels

in that sequence. We accordingly construct tables in that sequence. The first two tables follow;

Grade of Hotels

Standard	Superior	Luxury
70	80	50

The number 50 is derived by taking 70 and 80 from the total number of hotels. (200)

Location of Hotels

North	South	East	West
40	80	50	30

The number 30 is derived by taking 40, 80 and 50 from the total number of hotels (200)

The second two tables contain the information relation to the location of type of hotel;

Location of Luxury Hotels

North	South	East	West
5	30	10	5

The number 5 under North is derived by taking 30, 10 and 5 from the total number of luxury hotels. (50)

Location of Superior Hotels

North	South	East	West
15	35	20	10

The number 15 under North is derived by taking 35, 20 and 10 from the total number of superior hotels (80)

Finally, the complete table is constructed using the information contained in the previous four tables.

Location	GRADE			TOTAL
	Standard	Superior	Luxury	
North	20	15	5	40
South	15	35	30	80
East	20	20	10	50
West	15	10	5	30
TOTAL	70	80	50	200

The fifth row of numbers alongside TOTAL comes from the first table. The fourth column of numbers under TOTAL comes from the second table. The second and third columns of numbers come from the last two tables. Finally, the first column of numbers is derived from the following three columns. For example, there are 80 hotels in the south of which 15 are superior and 30 are luxury. Therefore, 15 must be standard, the number 15 being obtained by subtracting 35 and 30 from 80.

Chapter 5

2. Secondary data is data that is derived from primary data. Primary data is data that is collected first-hand from the situation being investigated.

Secondary statistics are numbers derived fropm secondary data in the form of totals, ratios and percentages.

4.

Deliveries Made in 1986

Period	Deliveries	Percentage Of Total
1st Quarter	1340	28
2nd Quarter	1210	26
3rd Quarter	1060	23
4th Quarter	1110	23
TOTAL	4720	100

Notice that the total number of deliveries made is given as **4720** whereas the total from the original table is **4726** which rounds to **4730**. This difference is called a **rounding error** and is unavoidable. The total in the table should always agree with the numbers in that table. Notice also the total percentage given as **100** - this is a check that the percentages have been calculated correctly.

6.

Frequencies of Scores						
		SCORE				
Goals	1	2	3	4	5	TOTAL
Number	8	12	7	13	10	50
%	16	24	14	26	20	100

Chapter 6

2. a) The following graph does not display a relationship between Datum 1 and Datum 2. Not only is it not possible to draw a smooth continuous line through all the points it is not even possible to draw a single line that approximates to all the points..

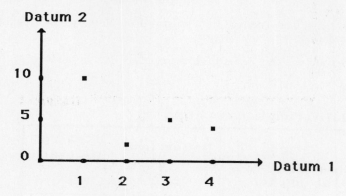

b) The following graph does display a relationship between Datum 1 and Datum 2. It is possible to draw a smooth continuous curve through all the points.

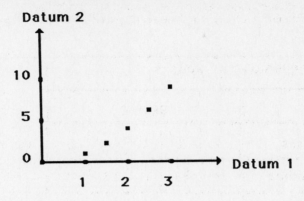

c) The following graph does display a relationship between Datum 1 and Datum 2. It is possible to draw a continuous straight line through all the points.

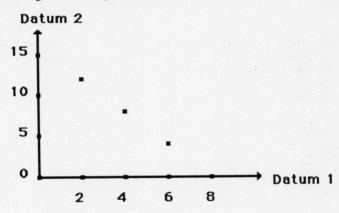

4. From the data in the question the following frequency table is constructed;

Frequency Table of Purchases

Group	Number of Purchases
0-1.9 gallons	6
2.0-3.9 gallons	8
4.0-5.9 gallons	13
6.0-7.9 gallons	10
8.0-9.9 gallons	8
TOTAL	45

From the data in the frequency table the following histogram was constructed;

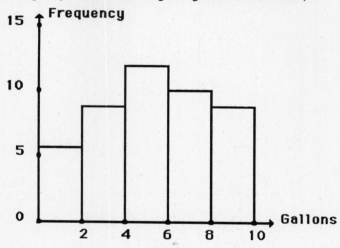

6. a) From the data in the question the following cumulative frequency table is constructed.

Number of Employees	% of all Companies	Cumulative	% of all Employees	Cumulative
Up to 49	10	10	5	5
50-99	20	30	15	20
100-499	35	65	35	55
500-999	20	85	20	75
1000+	15	100	25	100

b) From the data in this table the following Lorentz Graph is constructed.

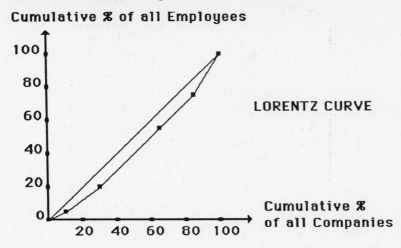

c) The single straight line represents the line of equal distribution of employees over companies. Because the Lorentz Curve departs from this straight line it is clear that the distribution of employees over companies is not equal. However, the departure from the single straight line is not too great which indicates that the departure from equal distribution is not too great.

Section 4

Chapter 1

2. a) Arranging the data in ascending order

1 1 1 1 1 1 2 2 2 2 2 2 2 3 3 3 3 3 3 4 4 4 4 4

we can see that there is an even number of numbers so there is no middle number. The **median** is then the average of the TWO middle numbers, which both happen to be 2. The median is 2

b) The mode is found by constructing a frequency table.

Number	Frequency
1	6
2	7
3	6
4	5
TOTAL	24

From this table we see that the number that occurs the MOST is 2. This means that the **mode** is 2.

4. The mean is found by adding all the scores together and dividing the result by the number of games played. The last 16 games played resulted in an AVERAGE SCORE of 1.25 goals. This means that the TOTAL SCORE from all these 165 games was

$$1.25 \times 16 = 20$$

The total number of goals scored during the first nine matches was

$$2 + 1 + 3 + 0 + 0 + 1 + 0 + 2 + 0 = 9$$

Consequently the total number of goals scored for ALL THE GAMES was

$$20 + 9 = 29$$

The were a total of **25** games (16 + 9) so the mean score for all the games was

$$29 \div 25 = 1.16$$

6. a) The lightest chocolate bar is 74.9 and the heaviest is 75.5. Since the weights are measured on a CONTINUOUS scale the frequency table will have to contain frequencies of GROUPS. These groups we shall take to be spreading over 0.1 grams. By counting the data we arrive at the following frequency table;

Weight	Frequency
74.9 and less than 75.0	10
75.0 and less than 75.1	12
75.1 and less than 75.2	11
75.2 and less than 75.3	7
75.3 and less than 75.4	6
75.4 and less than 75.5	3
75.5 and less than 75.6	1
TOTAL	50

b) Since the records were made to the nearest 0.1 gram it is possible that ROUNDING of the data has occurred. As a result, for example, a chocolate bar that was recorded as weighing 75.1 grams could have weighed anywhere between 75.05 grams and 75.14 grams. This means that the exact boundaries of the classes in the frequency table are as follows;

74.9 - 75.0　is　74.85 - 75.54
75.0 - 75.1　is　75.55 - 75.14
75.1 - 75.2　is　75.15 - 75.24
75.2 - 75.3　is　75.25 - 75.34
75.3 - 75.4　is　75.35 - 75.44
75.4 - 75.5　is　75.45 - 75.54
75.5 - 75.6　is　75.55 - 75.64

c) From the data in the previous table the following histogram was constructed;

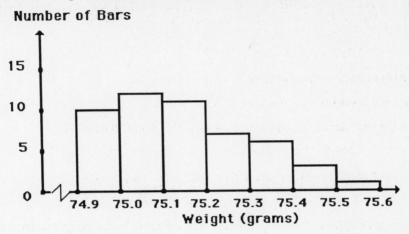

d) The mean weight is obtained by adding all the weights and dividing the result by 50. This mean weight is **75.1**. Since there is very little difference between the mean and the median further information can be obtained from the median measure of average. It tells us that there is a high concentration of chocolate bars with weights close to lower end of the weights.

Chapter 2

2. a) Within each class of Duration the average time of a call is taken to be the average of the shortest and the longest duration. This allows us to construct the following table that is used to calculate the average duration of all the calls.

Duration	Average Duration	Number of Calls	Total Time
under 3	1.5	45	67.5
3 to 6	4.5	59	265.5
6 to 9	7.5	38	285.0
9 to 12	10.5	31	325.5
12 to 15	13.5	19	256.5
15 to 18	16.5	8	132.0
TOTAL		200	1333.0

Average Duration
$$= 1333.0 \div 200$$
$$= 6.665 \text{ minutes}$$

The following table was constructed to calculate the standard deviation.

Duration	Deviation	(Deviation)^2	Number	Number x (Deviation)^2
1.5	-5.165	26.63	45	1198.15
4.5	-2.165	4.67	59	1455.52
7.5	+0.835	0.71	38	26.81
10.5	+3.835	14.75	31	457.11
13.5	+6.835	46.79	19	888.93
16.5	+9.835	96.83	8	774.61
		TOTAL		4801.13

$$\text{Variance} = 4801.13 \div 200$$
$$= 24.01$$

$$\text{Standard Deviation} = \sqrt{24.01}$$
$$= 4.9 \text{ minutes}$$

c) Coefficient of variation $= \text{Standard Deviation} \div \text{Mean}$
$$= 4.9 \div 6.665$$
$$= 0.74$$

4.

Delay	Average Delay	Number of Accounts	Total Delay
1 - 6	3.5	21	73.5
7 - 13	10	46	460.0
14-20	17	73	1241.0
21-27	24	27	648.0
28-34	31	24	744.0
35-41	38	9	342.0
TOTAL		200	3508.5

$$\text{MEAN} = 3508.5 \div 200$$
$$= 17.5 \text{ day}$$

Delay	Deviation	(Deviation)^2	Number	Number x (Deviation)^2
3.5	-14.0	196.00	21	4116.00
10	-7.5	56.25	46	2587.50
17	-0.5	0.25	73	18.25
24	6.5	42.25	27	1140.75
31	13.5	182.25	24	4374.00
38	20.5	420.25	9	3782.25
TOTAL			200	16018.75

$$\text{Variance} = 16018.75 \div 200$$
$$= 80.1$$

$$\text{Standard Deviation} = \sqrt{80.1}$$
$$= 8.95 \text{ days}$$

$$\text{Coefficient of variation} = 8.95 \div 18$$
$$= 0.5$$

6.

Mean Age	Males	Total Male Age	Females	Total Female Age
10	251	2510	241	2410
30.5	209	6374.5	215	6557.5
50.5	128	6464	128	6464
70.5	84	5922	95	6697.5
90.5	16	1448	24	2172
TOTAL	688	22718.5	703	24301

Average Male Age   = 22718.5 ÷ 688   = 33.0
Average Female Age = 24301 ÷ 703   = 34.6

MALES

Age	Deviation	(Deviation)^2	Number	Number x (Deviation)^2
10	-23	529	251	132779
30.5	-2.5	6.25	209	1306.25
50.5	+17.5	306.25	128	39200
70.5	+37.5	1406.25	84	118125
90.5	+57.5	3306.25	16	52900
		TOTAL	688	344310.25

$$\text{Variance} = 344310.25 \div 688$$
$$= 500.5$$

$$\text{Standard Deviation} = \sqrt{500.5}$$
$$= 22.4$$

$$\text{Coefficient of Variation} = 22.4 \div 33$$
$$= 0.68$$

273

FEMALES

Age	Deviation	(Deviation)^2	Number	Number x (Deviation)^2
10	-24.6	605.16	241	145843.56
30.5	-4.1	16.81	215	3614.15
50.5	+15.9	252.81	128	32359.68
70.5	+35.9	1288.81	95	122436.95
90.5	+55.9	3124.81	24	74995.44
		TOTAL	703	379249.78

$$\text{Variance} = 379249.78 \div 703$$
$$= 539.5$$

$$\text{Standard Deviation} = \sqrt{539.5}$$
$$= 22.2$$

$$\text{Coefficient of Variation} = 22.2 \div 34.6$$
$$= 0.64$$

Since the MALES have the lowest coefficient of variation the MALE'S ages vary less than the FEMALE'S ages.

Chapter 3

2. a) **Range** = Highest value - Lowest value

$$= (25.5 - 19.5) \text{ mm}$$

$$= 6 \text{ mm}$$

b) Lower Quartile

If the eggs were ranked in ascending order the position of the lower quartile egg would be

$$(100 + 1) \div 4 = 25.25 \text{ position in the ranking}$$

Since uor reading cannot be so accurate we shall take this position to be 25th in the ranking. Reading off the 25th egg we find the size of the lower quartile egg is

$$Q_1 = 22 \text{ mm}$$

Median

Similary the median egg is located at the

$$(100 + 1)/2 = 50.5 \text{ position in the ranking}$$

We take this to be the 50th egg. Thus the median egg size is

$$M = 22.5 \text{ mm}$$

Upper Quartile

The upper quartile egg is located at the

$3 \times (100 + 1)/4 = 75.75$ position in the ranking

We take this to be the 75th egg. Thus the upper quartile egg size is

$$Q_3 = 23.5$$

These results tell us that

1/4 of the eggs were between 19.5 mm and 22 mm long (a 2.5 mm spread)

1/4 of the eggs were between 23.5 mm and 25.5 mm (a 2 mm spread)

1/2 of the eggs were between 22 mm and 23.5 mm (a 1.5 mm spread which is only 1/4 of the range)

The median is a good measure of central tendency as it fall within the spread of egg sizes occupied by half of the eggs.

c) Most cockoo eggs lie between 22 mm and 24 mm in length.

d) Had the horizontal axis not been 'broken' the graph would have been squashed into the right hand side of the horizontal axis. This would have made the graph harder to read as it would have been smaller to be accomodated on the page.

e) Not at all confident. The quartile deviation is

$$(Q_3 - Q_1) \div 2 = (23.5 - 22) \div 2$$
$$= 0.75$$

which is a very small proportion of the range. Since half of the measured eggs lie between the two quartiles and since this spread is so small any eggs lying outside the range are most unlikely to be cuckoo eggs.

4. The cumulative frequency table is given as follows;

Range of Marks	Frequency	Cumulative
0 and less than 10	4	4
10 and less than 20	5	9
20 and less than 30	3	12
30 and less than 40	4	16
40 and less than 50	8	24
50 and less than 60	9	33
60 and less than 70	11	44
70 and less than 80	8	52
80 and less than 90	6	58
90 to 100	2	60

From the data in this table the following CUMULATIVE FREQUENCY graph is constructed.

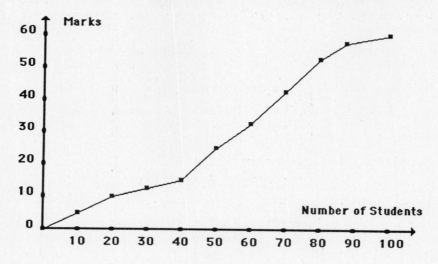

The points have been plotted at the TOP of each range of marks. For instance, the range 0 to less than 30 marks has the point plotted at 30 because all those cumulative marks are LESS THAN 30. To be exact the point should be plotted at 29.4 because the marks are recorded to the nearest whole mark so some ROUNDING could have been performed. thw value of 29.4 is the highest mark than will be ROUNDED DOWN to less than 30. The next mark of 29.5 will be ROUNDED UP to 30.

276

b) Reading from this graph the position of the 10th percentile is

$$10 \times (60 + 1) \div 100 = 6.1 \text{ in the ranked marks}$$

Reading from the 6th position on the vertical axis across to the curve and then down to the horixontal axis gives the 10th percentile mark as

$$P_{10} = 14.5$$

Similarly, the position of the 90th percentile mark is

$$90 \times (60 + 1) \div 100 = 54.9 \text{ in the ranked marks}$$

Reading from the 55th position on the vertical axis across to the curve and then down to the horizontal axis gives the 90th percentile as

$$P_{90} = 85$$

c) By the very definition of percentiles half of the student's marks lie between the 25th and the 75th percentiles. that is **30.**

6. The data can be counted to produce the following cumulative frequency table;

Faults	Cumulative Frequency
1 or less	17
2 or less	21
3 or less	26
4 or less	35
5 or less	40

From the data in this table the following graph can be constructed;

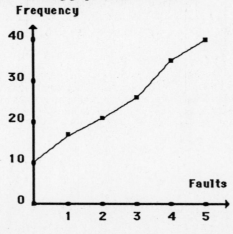

a) **4th Decile**

The position of the 4th decile is

$$4 \times (40 + 1) \div 10 = 16.4 \text{ in the ranked data}$$

Reading this off the vertical axis, across to the curve and then down to the horizontal axis gives the value of the **4th decile** as

0.88 faults

The position of the 8th decile is

$$8 \times (40 + 1) \div 10 = 32.8 \text{ in the ranked data}$$

Reading off 32.8 on the vertical axis, across to the curve and down to the horizontal axis give the 87th decile as

3.76 faults

b) **Ranked Data**

0 0 0 0 0 0 0 0 0 0 0 0
1 1 1 1 1
2 2 2 2
3 3 3 3 3
4 4 4 4 4 4 4 4 4
5 5 5 5 5

The position of the 4th decile is at 16.4 in the ranking. The 16th and the 17th numbers are both 1 so the 4th decile is 1.

The position of the 8th decile is at 32.8 in the ranking. The 32nd and the 33rd numbers are both 4 so the 8th decile is 4

The latter two numbers found for the 4th and 8th deciles are the correct ones. The first set of two numbers found from the graph were obtained on the assumption that there was a CONTINUOUS range of numbers of faults whereas the numbers of faults are actually DISCRETE.

Chapter 4

a) The OTHER column should read;

Other

74
80
74
88
116

Wheat	Barley	Potatoes	Beet	Other	TOTAL
100	100	100	100	100	100
122	127	101	89	108	547
110	115	66	61	100	452
130	153	94	92	119	588
192	156	106	92	157	703

4. a) 1975 is the BASE YEAR against which other years are compared

b) $(95 \times 100) \div 129 = 73.6$

       74 to the same level of significance as the rest of the table.

c)

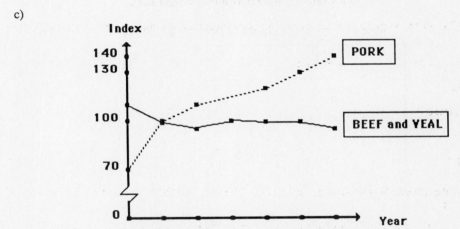

d) **Instant Coffee**

From the table : 32 58   88 100 72 102 104

Becomes :   100 181 152 114 72 133 102

e)

Chapter 5

2. a)

Year	Numbers
1976	13,800
1977	-
1978	13,800
1979	14.300
1980	14,800
1981	14,900
1982	15,300
1983	15,500

b)

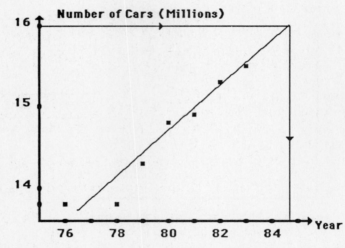

d) Assuming the numbers set against each year are set at the year end, the number of cars can be expected to exceed 16 million during 1985. Because the last five points are close to the line of best fit this estimate should be quite accurate if the behaviour during those last five years is repeated during the following two years.

4.a)

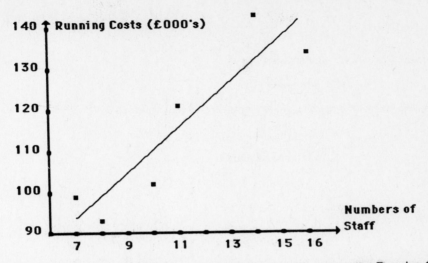

b) We let the variable x represent Number of Staff and the variable y represent Running Costs in £ 000's

x	y	xy	x^2
7	99	693	49
8	93	744	64
10	102	1020	100
11	121	1331	121
14	143	2002	196
16	136	2176	256
TOTAL 66	694	7966	786

Using the formulae for the regression line;

$$n = 5$$

$$b = \frac{(5) \times (7966) - (66) \times (694)}{(5) \times (786) - (66) \times (66)}$$

$$= 14$$

$$a = \frac{694}{5} - 14 \times \frac{66}{5}$$

$$= -46$$

This gives the equation of the regression line as

$$y = 14x - 46$$

c) The running costs of a regional office employing 12 staff will then be

$$y = 14 \times 12 - 46$$

$$= 122 \text{ thousand pounds}$$

Chapter 6

2.a)

b)

x	y	xy	x^2	y^2
6	21	126	36	441
11	18	198	121	324
12	33	396	144	1089
9	39	351	81	1521
11	25	275	121	625
7	27	189	49	729
9	21	189	81	441
65	184	1724	633	5170

$$r = \frac{\{(7)(1724) - (65)(184)\}}{[\{(7)(633)-(65)(65)\}\{(7)(5170)-(184)(184)\}]^{1/2}}$$

$$= 0.115$$

c) There is very little correlation between the number of staff and the value of sales.

4.

	1	2	d	d^2
1	4	4	0	0
2	2	2	0	0
3	8	1	7	49
4	1	5	-4	16
5	5	3	2	4
6	6	7	-1	1
7	3	8	-5	25
8	10	9	1	1
9	7	6	1	1
10	9	10	-1	1
			TOTAL	**98**

$$r_s = 1 - (6 \times 98) \div (10 \times [100 - 1])$$

$$= 0.41$$

This value of the rank correlation coefficient shows that there was moderate agreement between the two panel members.

Chapter 7

2.   The following table is used to produce both the trend and the seasonal factors.

Houses	Moving Total	Average Total	TREND	Fluctuation
135				
198	671			
182		659.5	165	17
156	648	639.5	160	-4
112	631	619.0	155	-43
181	607	594.5	149	32
158	582	570.0	143	15
131	558	549.5	137	-6
88	541	533.5	133	-45
164	526	514	129	35
143	502			
107				

Table of Fluctuations

	Q1	Q2	Q3	Q4
1981			17	-4
1982	-43	32	15	-6
1983	-45	35		
TOTAL	-88	67	32	-10
AVERAGE	-44	33.5	16	-5

If we were to subtract these quarterly fluctuations from corresponding future quarterly figures they would balance out the seasonal fluctuations. However, because the sum of the four fluctuations equals 0.5 the effect of using them as seasonal factors in any one year would be to add a 0.5 contribution to the total year. To avoid adding such a net contribution to the year we can share the 0.5 out amongst the four averages - by subtracting 1.25 from each of them. Their sum would then be zero. Since 1.25 houses is not a significant amount over one quarter we shall take the four unadjusted averages to be our seasonal factors.

We now apply them to the data obtained from the following graph of seasonally adjusted figures.

Quarter	Houses (TREND)
1981 Q3	165
Q4	160
1982 Q1	155
Q2	149
Q3	143
Q4	137
1983 Q1	133
Q2	129
Q3	143 - 16 = 127
Q4	107 + 5 = 112

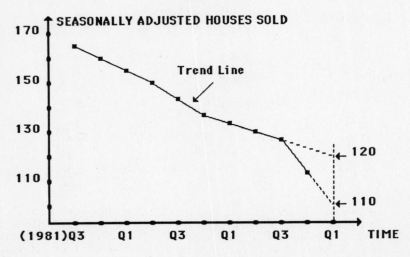

284

The graph exhibits two possibilities. The adjusted fourth quarter sales figure departs from the previous trend line quite dramatically. We can assume this dramatic departure to be a freak in which case we just extend the trend line from the previous four quarters to produce an anticipates seasonally adjusted sale in the first quarter of 1984 of 120 houses. To de-seasonalise this figure we ADD the seasonal factor for the first quarter which is -44. This gives us an anticipated sale of 76 houses in the first quarter of 1984. If, however, we do not accept the last point plotted on the graph to be a freak then we must extend the trend line down to the number 110. De-seasonalising this number we would anticipate the number of houses sold in the first quarter of 1984 to be 110 - 44 = 66.

In conclusion, the best estimate that we can give for the stated quarter is somewhere between 66 and 76 houses sold.

4. The following table is used to produce both the trend and the seasonal factors.

Computers	Moving Total	Average Total	TREND	Fluctuation
77.5				
63.2				
	274.0			
54.8		275.4	68.8	-14
	276.7			
78.5		278.1	69.5	9
	279.5			
80.2		281.8	70.4	9.8
	284.0			
66.0		287.1	71.8	-5.8
	290.2			
59.3		292.0	73.0	-13.7
	293.8			
84.7		295.0	73.8	10.8
	296.2			
83.8		297.6	74.4	9.4
	299.0			
68.4		301.8	75.5	-7.1
	304.6			
62.1				
90.3				

Table of Fluctuations

	Q1	Q2	Q3	Q4
1979			-14	9
1980	9.8	-5.8	-13.7	10.8
1981	9.4	-7.1		
TOTAL	19.2	-12.9	-27.7	19.8
AVERAGE	9.6	-6.45	-13.85	9.9

If we were to subtract these quarterly fluctuations from corresponding future quarterly figures they would balance out the seasonal fluctuations. However, because the sum of the four fluctuations equals -0.8 the effect of using them as seasonal factors in any one year would be to add a -0.8 contribution to the total year. To avoid adding such a net contribution to the year we can share the -0.8 out amongst the four averages - by adding 0.2 to each of them. Their sum will then be zero. The adjusted seasonal factors are then

Q1	Q2	Q3	Q4
9.8	-6.25	-13.65	10.1 (Sum = 0)

We now apply them to the data obtained from the following graph of seasonally adjusted figures.

Quarter	Sales (TREND)
1979 Q3	68.8
Q4	69.5
1980 Q1	70.4
Q2	71.8
Q3	73.0
Q4	73.8
1981 Q1	74.7
Q2	75.5
Q3	62.1 + 13.65 = 75.8 (rounded)
Q4	90.3 - 10.1　= 80.2

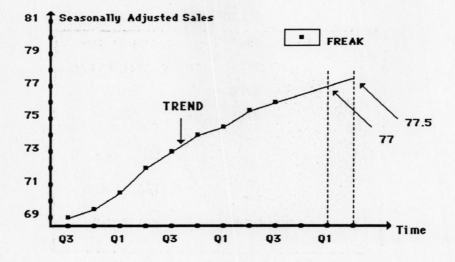

The graph exhibits two possibilities. The adjusted fourth quarter sales figure departs from the previous trend line quite dramatically. Because the departure is so great we can assume this dramatic departure to be a freak in which case we just extend the trend line from the previous two quarters to produce an anticipates seasonally adjusted sale in the first quarter of 1982 of £77,000 and in the second quarter of 1982 of £77,500. To de-seasonalise these figures we ADD the seasonal factors for the first and second quarters which are 9.8 and -6.3(rounded) respectively. This gives us anticipated sales to the values of £88,800 and £71,200 in the first and second quarters of 1982 respectively

Section 5

Chapter 1

2.

	Sales (£0,000)			TOTAL	%
	Gears	Valves	Pumps		
1981	12	27	28	67	24
1982	15	31	59	105	37
1983	13	15	82	110	39
TOTAL	40	73	169	282	100

4.

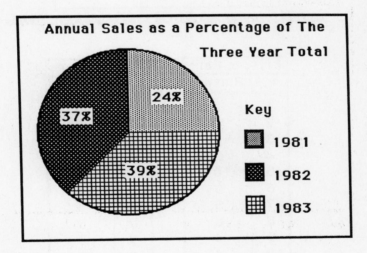

Annual Sales as a Percentage of The Three Year Total

24%
37%
39%

Key
1981
1982
1983

Chapter 2

2.

Population of England and Wales (00,000's)

Age Group	1951	1981
Under 5	37	29
5 – 14	60	71
15 – 29	90	109
30 – 44	98	95
45 – 64	106	109
65 – 74	33	45
74 +	16	28
TOTAL	440	486

Source: Office of Population Censuses and Statistics

4. a)

British Cars		Foreign Cars	
Age	Number	Age	Number
1	7	1	8
2	9	2	8
3	6	3	5
4	5	4	4
5	10	5	5
6	9	6	4
7	5	7	3
8	6	8	2
9	4	9	3
10	4	10	3
11	3	11	2
12	4	12	1

b) **Foreign Cars Mean Age**

$= (8x1+8x2+5x3+4x4+5x5+4x6+3x7+2x8+3x9+3x10+2x11+1x12) + 48$

$= 4.83$ years

Foreign Cars Median Age

= (Age of 24th Car + Age of 25th Car) ÷ 2

= 4 years

c)

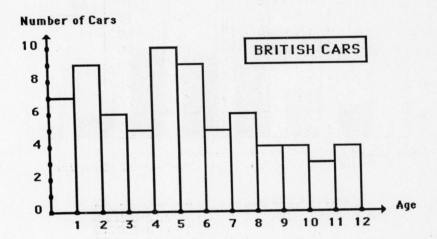

The histogram is appropriate because it clearly displays relative sizes. the number of cars of a particular year is proportional to the area of the rectangle constructed on that year. The intervals are appropriate because those were the categories in which the data was gathered - a car's age being determined by the single letter in the registration number.

d)

Record of Cars By Age and Origin

	British	Foreign	TOTAL
Newer[1]	37	30	67
Older[2]	35	18	53
TOTAL	72	48	120

1 Newer refers to cars 5 years old or less

2 Older refers to all cars older than 5 years

There are clearly more British cars than Foreign. However, since there are almost twice as many 'Newer' Foreign cars than 'Older' whereas the numbers of 'Newer' and 'Older' British cars are almost the same it would appear that significantly more people are opting for imported cars than were in the past.

Chapter 3

2.

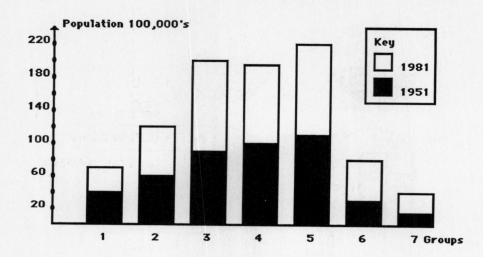

4.a)

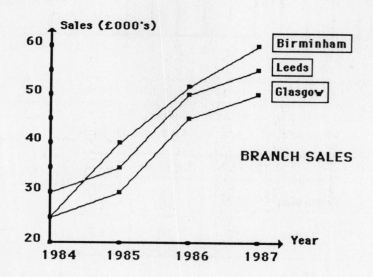

b)

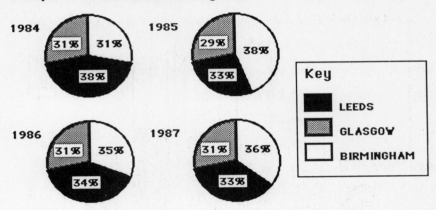

Comparison of Branches by Year

1984   31%   31%   38%

1985   29%   38%   33%

1986   31%   35%   34%

1987   31%   36%   33%

Key

■ LEEDS

▨ GLASGOW

□ BIRMINGHAM

c)

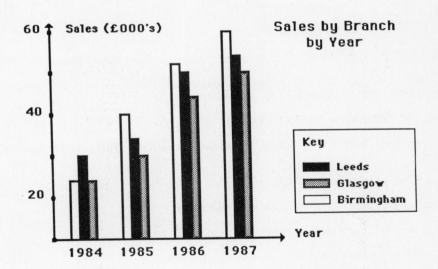

Sales by Branch by Year

Sales (£000's)

Key

■ Leeds

▨ Glasgow

□ Birmingham

Year — 1984 1985 1986 1987

Appendix

2. a) There are **4** aces in a pack of **52** playing cards so there are 4 chances out of 52 of drawing an ace. The required probability is, therefore, **4/52 = 1/13.**

b) There are **26** red cards in a deck. The probability of drawing a red card is **26/52 = 0.5**

c) There is only **1** Jack of Clubs so the probability of drawing it is **1/52.**

d) There are **2** black sevens so the probability of drawing a black seven is

$$\text{Pr(Black Seven) = 2/52.}$$

The complement of drawing a black seven is NOT drawing a black seven. Thus

$$\text{Pr(NOT a Black Seven) = 1 - Pr(Black Seven)}$$

$$= 1 - 2/52$$

$$= 50/52.$$

e) There are **2** red fours and **2** black twos. Thus,

Similarly **Pr(NOT a Two) = 48/52.** Hence,

Pr(NOT a Four AND NOT A Two) = Pr(NOT A Four) x Pr(NOT A Two)

$$= (48/52) \text{ x } (48/52)$$

$$= 144/169.$$

d) The situation where AT LEAST ONE of the two cards was a King can occur in one of three ways.

1. The first card was a king with probability **4/52** and the second card was NOT a King with probability **48/52.** This combination has the probability;

Pr(A King AND NOT A King) = (4/52) x (48/52)

2. The first card was NOT a King and the second card was a King. This situation has the probability;

Pr(NOT A King AND A King) = (48/52) x (4/52)

3. Both cards were Kings. This will occur with probability;

Pr(A King AND A King) = (4/52) x (4/52).

The probability that at least one of the cards was a King is then;

Pr({A King AND NOT A King} OR {NOT A King AND A King} OR {A King AND A King})

= {(4/52) x (48/52)} + {(48/52) x (4/52)} + {(4/52) x (4/52)}

= **400/2704** ·

e) YES the results would have been different. Had the first card not been replaced the deck would then have only 51 cards in it. This would change the probabilities for the second draw. If the first card is not replaced the selection of the second card DEPENDS upon which card was selected first.

Pr(Red Four) = 2/52 and Pr(Black Two) = 2/52

So

Pr(Red Four OR Black TWO) = Pr(Red Four) + Pr(Black Two)

$$= 2/52 + 2/52$$

$$= 4/52.$$

f) Pr(Queen of Diamonds) = 1/52 and Pr(Ace of Hearts) = 1/52

thus

Pr(Queen of Diamonds OR Ace of Hearts)

$$= Pr(Queen of Diamonds) + Pr(Ace of Hearts)$$

$$= 1/52 + 1/52$$

$$= 2/52.$$

4. a) Pr(An Ace AND An Ace) = Pr(An Ace) x Pr(An Ace)

$$= (4/52) x (4/52)$$

$$= 1/169.$$

By replacing the first drawn card back into the deck the second draw is INDEPENDENT of the first.

b) Pr(Red Card AND Red Card) = Pr(Red Card) x Pr(Red Card)

$$= (26/52) x (26/52)$$

$$= 1/4.$$

c) Pr(A Four) = 4/52 therefore

Pr(NOT A Four) = 1 - Pr(A Four)

= 1 - 4/52

= 48/52

INDEX

(The reference number S.C:PP refers to SECTION.CHAPTER:PARAGRAPH)